Let's Target

Comprehension

8

D1455971

TEACHERS AT WORK

Sadlier School

Comprehension

Teachers at work™ an imprint of Sadlier School, was created by teachers with teachers in mind to provide the right materials to support students with achieving academic success. Teachers all over the country contributed their ideas and expertise to bring together opportunities for students to practice essential skills and strategies with engaging print and online resources. Together they built a program that will support both teachers and students. We are excited to share these engaging print and online resources with you.

Sadlier School

Cover Series Design: Studio Montage, St. Louis, MO, United States of America

For additional online resources, go to sadlierconnect.com.

 is a trademark of William H. Sadlier, Inc.

William H. Sadlier, Inc.
9 Pine Street
New York, NY 10005-4700

Printed in the U.S.A.
ISBN: 978-1-4217-4728-6
1 2 3 4 5 6 7 8 9   19 18 17 16 15

PREFACE

....

Welcome to the *Let's Target*™ Series

Teachers at work™ is excited to introduce this new series to support students in mastering the Common Core State Standards.

The *Let's Target* series was developed by teachers. We understand students need to be engaged in their learning to succeed. **"I got it!"** That's what we want students to say when they focus on the lessons in the *Let's Target* series. As teachers, we know how hard it can be to find the right material to boost student achievement. With the *Let's Target* series, students complete the exercises in the book and then go online to reinforce what they have learned.

Want to flip it? Go ahead! Begin with the online resources to jumpstart the learning and then complement the activities with lessons from the book. Either way, students and teachers will be happy to get more opportunities to learn and practice essential skills.

Do you want to work independently or with a peer? *Let's Target* allows for all different kinds of learning strategies. Teachers will find more guidance about this in their Teacher's Guides.

Getting ready for Common Core Assessments? *Let's Target Comprehension* provides opportunities for students to read more complex text and apply comprehension strategies across different content-area topics.

***Let's Target Comprehension* for summer learning?** With *Let's Target Comprehension*, students will have a broad range of text themes and genres that will allow them to read widely and deeply and come back to school ready for success!

The components of the *Let's Target* series include:
- Student Editions with lots of opportunities for **"I got it!"** moments
- Teacher's Guides which support teachers with **CCSS connections** and problem solutions
- Online Resources give students and teachers the tools to **blend learning** and engage in learning in the classroom and at home

Teachers from around the country collaborated through **Teachers at work** ™, contributing ideas and expertise, to develop this series to prepare students for academic success. Please let us know if you have any ideas that will support students in reaching school success! Contact us at TeachersAtWork@Sadlier.com.

Teachers at work

CONTENTS

BASIC

INTERMEDIATE

ADVANCED

NOTE:

Let's Target Comprehension is designed for students to practice and gain proficiency in answering the different types of comprehension questions found in the multiple-choice and open-ended formats.

The passages are analyzed and categorized into *Basic, Intermediate,* and *Advanced.*

The **Basic** level aims to increase student's expertise in making meaning.

In the **Intermediate** level, the passages encourage higher-level thinking and analytical levels of comprehension.

The **Advanced** level encourages students to think beyond the ideas presented in the passages, develop deep comprehension, and prepare students for high-level comprehension of complex texts.

EXERCISE 1

/12
points

Read the passage carefully.

Best Friends

"Come on, let's go paint the town red..." Chloe's mother sang along to the radio blasting in the kitchen. Chloe covered her ears. It was not that she disliked her mother's singing, but the song, which was her mother's favorite, had been played for the thousandth time in the past few days. Why did radio stations play popular
5   songs so frequently? Soon, all the listeners would detest them and they would no longer be popular.

"I'm going to Jasmine's house, mom," Chloe called over her shoulder before she opened the main door. At least over at Jasmine's house, she would not have to listen to the same song blasting from the radio. Jasmine's house did not even
10   have a radio. Her parents believed in having minimal items in the house. In fact her house was so bare that they sat on rugs and cushions in the living room and ate on the floor with just a piece of newspaper. They were not poor, just into what Jasmine had told her was called 'minimalist'.

She knocked on Jasmine's door with the brass knocker that hung in the middle
15   of the lime green door. They did not believe in doorbells either. The door was flung open seconds later and her friend, Jasmine, stood before her in a pair of tattered denim shorts and a T-shirt that said "I didn't do it." "You came just at the right time," she gushed as she dragged Chloe into her house. "Mum is making her own toilet cleaner using soap that we got from Christmas last year. Come on in and
20   help. You can make it in any shape you like and you can take it home with you."

Chloe grinned. The enthusiasm emanating from Jasmine was infectious. Ironically, her mother had just bought the latest toilet cleaner designed to clean toilets better than any other cleaner could. In the middle of the kitchen counter, Jasmine's mother sat with huge bars of soap and a small penknife. "Hi, Chloe.
25   Would you like to join us? We are making a toilet cleaner. I heard about it from a friend of mine and I thought why not? It would be a good way to use all that soap Grandma Joan gave us last Christmas."

It was an afternoon of constant carving that caused blisters on Chloe's fingers. She was glad when she was finally done. She was not very proud of her handiwork for the heart shaped soap did not look the way it was supposed to and was definitely not anything like those she had seen in the shops but Jasmine and her mother clapped their hands in delight and told Chloe that she had done a fantastic job. "I think it's fantastic, Chloe!" Jasmine's mother beamed at her. Chloe grinned. It was just like her to compliment others. It was their constant optimism that had drawn her to Jasmine in the first place when they first knew each other in school. Chloe had done badly on a test and Jasmine had offered to help her. Consequently, the girls spent a lot of time after school doing their homework together.

It was apparent from the start that Jasmine's house was more conducive. The lack of curtains brought in the natural light and it was a much airier and cheerier place to complete their daily homework. No matter what Chloe did to let the light in, her house always seemed gloomy and she had to turn on the lights even in the day. She raised the blinds and opened the windows wide but without the lights turned on, a shadow was cast over the entire living room – the place that allowed in the most light in the house. Chloe found it dull doing her homework and she often fell asleep before she completed it. Homework did not seem as dreary for it led to activities like arts and crafts which Jasmine's mother was a natural in. She could make use of any material lying around in the house, turning it into something unique and useful. Sometimes she conducted classes and Chloe found out that the classes brought in the money that was required for the school books that Jasmine needed. Her life was simple but she was content. Chloe had almost everything she wanted and she had always thought that she was living a privileged life but she soon realized that her mother's lack of interaction with Jasmine's parents and the like was because she scoffed at them and mocked their lifestyle. Chloe began to despise the way her mother viewed the people around her. The good-heartedness of Jasmine's family touched her. On several occasions, she went to the Kind Hearts Center to help with the cooking and distribution of food to the poor and homeless. It was hard work and by the time Chloe left the center with Jasmine and her parents, she understood what it meant to be on one's feet the whole day. A week after Chloe told her mother about her first visit to the center, she noticed her mother writing a check for the Kind Hearts Center. Chloe knew the importance of donations to these centers but she could not help wondering if her mother's actions were in any way a reaction to what Jasmine and her family had done for the needy.

"We're going to the zoo tomorrow. Do you want to join us? Dad's friend works at the zoo. We can see how the keepers take care of the zoo after closing time. It will be fun!" Jasmine's eyes shone like she had won a prize in a drawing. Chloe nodded. A day out with Jasmine and her family would always be a day to remember.

Choose the correct answer and circle the correct letter.

1 What is the first impression the reader has of Chloe's relationship with her mother?
- A   They avoid talking to each other
- B   Chloe enjoys her mother's company.
- C   There are possible conflicts between them.
- D   Chloe's mother does not take good care of her daughter.

2 The word "minimalist" (line 13) tells you that Jasmine's family is _____.
- A   thrifty
- B   simple
- C   humble
- D   modern

3 Which of the following supports the conclusion that Jasmine was a lively girl?
- A   "Come on in and help" (lines 19-20)
- B   "dragged Chloe into her house" (line 18)
- C   "door was flung open seconds later" (lines 15-16)
- D   "stood before her in a pair of tattered denim shorts" (lines 16-17)

4 "Ironically, her mother had just bought the latest toilet cleaner designed to clean toilets better than any other cleaner could." (lines 22-23)
Why was this information included in the story?
- A   To make comparisons between Chloe's and Jasmine's family
- B   To show that Chloe's mother was overly concerned with hygiene
- C   To explain why Chloe preferred to be with Jasmine's family
- D   To increase tension between Chloe and her mother

5 "We are making a toilet cleaner. I heard about it from a friend of mine and I thought why not? It would be a good way to use all that soap Grandma Joan gave us last Christmas." (lines 25-27)
What is the main conclusion the reader can draw about Jasmine's mother from the sentences above?
- A   She did not like to receive gifts.
- B   She did not let things go to waste.
- C   She listened to her friends' advice.
- D   She enjoyed doing arts and crafts.

6 What effect does the author create by repeating that Chloe's work was "fantastic" (lines 32 and 33)?

A   The author emphasizes the positive outlook Jasmine's family had.

B   The author explains how Jasmine's family treats their friends.

C   The author highlights the most important characteristic of families.

D   The author portrays the close relationship between Chloe and Jasmine's family.

7 The author says "Jasmine's house was more conducive." (line 38) Explain how this benefited Chloe. Support your answer with details from the passage.

_____

_____

_____

_____

_____

_____

_____

_____

_____

_____

_____

_____

_____

_____

_____

_____

_____

8 (a) What is the main idea in the story?

A   It is important to have good friends.

B   Some homes are better decorated than others.

C   True happiness can only be found with one's family.

D   It is possible to be happy even if one leads a simple life.

(b) The author states that Chloe led "a privileged life." (line 51) Explain how this phrase and the answer in Part A contributes to the author's portrayal of happy families.

_____

_____

_____

_____

_____

_____

_____

_____

_____

_____

_____

_____

_____

_____

_____

9 What impact does Chloe's opinion of helping the needy have on the development of the story?

A   It emphasizes that money is not the best way to solve problems.

B   It explains why Chloe did not enjoy staying home.

C   It highlights Chloe's kindheartedness.

D   It heightens the problems Chloe faced in her daily life.

10 (a) Why did the author use "like she had won a prize in a drawing" (line 66) to describe Jasmine's feelings?

A   It showed how excited Jasmine was.

B   It compared Jasmine's to Chloe's reaction.

C   It showed that Jasmine had a kindhearted personality.

D   It revealed that Chloe did not understand how Jasmine was feeling.

(b) Besides the answer in Part A, what else does the simile reveal to the reader about outings for Jasmine's family? Support your answer with details from the passage.

_____

_____

_____

_____

_____

_____

_____

_____

_____

_____

_____

_____

_____

_____

_____

_____

_____

_____

_____

_____

Glossary

blasting: very loud noise
Music was blasting from the house at the end of the street as a party was on.

infectious: referring to feelings that can spread quickly from one person to another
She had such an infectious smile that I could not help smiling back at her.

apparent: obvious
It was apparent that the group would have problems completing the project when the group members could not get along with one another.

BASIC

EXERCISE 2

/12
points

Read the passage carefully.

Emotions

We experience a gamut of emotions every day that can range from ecstasy to utter despair. Seeing how we face a variety of situations every day, it is rational that our feelings change, sometimes widely in just one day. The often asked question "How are you feeling today?" leads us to focus on that one particular emotion that
5   perhaps dominates most of our day. Yet, we cannot ignore the other feelings, no matter how minute, that creep into our lives, linger and perhaps vanish later only to be replaced by another feeling.

Our dominant mood or emotion for a particular day often stems from the feeling that seems to overwhelm us. Perhaps it was an important event that created that
10 feeling; perhaps it was a particularly startling event. Note that a dominant mood could be both a positive as well as a negative one. An employee who receives news of his promotion once he goes to work could be in seventh heaven the entire day. Nothing that happens could dampen his mood. A person who has to deal with the sudden death of a loved one could be so devastated that nothing can lift his spirits,
15 not just for that day but perhaps for days to come.

What happens then when a particular feeling dominates our moods for that day? We tend to view our everyday events in a different light. For example, someone who suffers from sudden grief might not be willing to visit the places he usually enjoys or eat the food he usually likes. Nothing will seem appealing to him. In
20 extreme cases, the low feelings might cause him to withdraw from everyone else. This behavior might exacerbate his thoughts or help him to heal. An overwhelming sense of happiness provides the cushion against events that might otherwise cause irritation. For example, a lady who is so pleased that her child scored the winning goal for the school might not be annoyed by the drivers who hindered her drive
25 home that day. She might even turn the event into a positive one by being more patient towards her fellow drivers.

Sadlier School

What these tell us is that positive feelings have better outcomes in people's lives than negative feelings. As we have often heard- when we are happy, the whole world smiles with us. Yet, when we are upset, numerous quotes remind us to pick ourselves up. No one wants to be with a person who is experiencing a negative feeling. It is no wonder that negative feelings are often frowned upon and anyone experiencing long bouts of negativity is naturally expected to seek help. Ask people which type of feeling they would rather experience and the answer would not just be unanimous but also immediate – happy, positive feelings. On a larger scale, if everyone in the world were happy and contented, there would probably not be conflict and wars.

However, this does not mean that we should negate the negative emotions that we feel. We cannot run away from negative feelings if we are faced with certain situations. For example, students might be worried about how they would fare on a test; parents might be worried about their children's safety during the day when they are in school; we might be envious of the success our friends seem to be achieving; we might be furious with our neighbor for not cleaning up the mess his dog left behind on the sidewalk. The list goes on. Some of them are the result of minor inconveniences that we push to the back of our minds once the incident is over. We might grumble about them but they do not cause any drastic impact on how we lead the rest of our day. Some of them might affect us more and it is these that are important and can perhaps be the perfect driving force of our future actions.

Fear is a common negative emotion that many people experience, sometimes even daily. It is something that we try to suppress or ignore at times, hoping that this negative feeling will somehow go away. However, it is fear that helps us to make better plans and to be wary of the things that could lead us to feeling fearful. It is certainly not a weakness as some might see it but an emotion that can be turned into a strength for leading a more meaningful life. For example, if we are afraid of being accosted by a stranger while walking through a park late at night, we might then make plans to return home earlier when it is still bright or when the park is not deserted. We might also find another route to get home so that we can avoid having an unpleasant meeting with a stranger. Closely related to fear is worry and anxiety. For example, someone might worry about losing his job. The anxiety he faces about being unemployed might propel him to work harder. He might be more conscientious about completing his work on time and ensuring that he meets his supervisor's expectations.

Another negative feeling is frustration. When someone is frustrated by the events that take place in a day, he might become angry or he might despair. Whatever the end result of this is, his frustration could force him to examine the causes of the situation he is in. For example, if a student is frustrated about having to complete work that he does not understand, he might be motivated to do more research to clear up any doubts he has. Continued frustration is an even bigger motivation for improvement than one-off minor frustrations. For example, someone who is frustrated about being stuck in a job he abhors, might be motivated to look even harder for another job. He might also take a step back to examine his own personality so that he can find a job that is more suitable for himself.

Perhaps the most common negative feeling is anger. This is also a feeling that people might try to suppress. We see daily incidents of how anger can lead to problems such as conflict and war. Anger can cause rash actions that lead to the needless deaths of many innocent people. However, it is also anger that causes people to voice their opinions and to fight for changes. For example, people who take part in rallies, voicing their dissatisfaction about policies they are displeased with are expressing their anger. Their demonstrations might result in a change of policies, thereby improving the lives of millions of people. If a parent is displeased with a child, voicing that anger will also tell the child that he has done something wrong and in the process make him aware of important values. Why then should anger be seen in a negative light? The main reason for this is that anger when taken to the extreme can cause great harm. It is extreme anger that results in a disproportionate reaction to a situation. For example, someone who is very angry with his sibling for spoiling his toy might decide to use violence to dissipate his anger. This could result in him injuring his sibling for an incident that could be solved in a calmer manner resulting in a less undesirable outcome.

In other words, it is not that negative feelings should be suppressed or thought of in a negative light but that such feelings need to be better managed by every individual. Anger management is the buzzword today, relevant for everyone from the child to the elderly. Feel angry, but learn how to control the temper, a by-product of anger, so that it does not manifest itself into something that could cause great harm to others.

The next time you experience an

95 overwhelming feeling of happiness or anger, take the time to find out why you are experiencing such feelings before acting on them. Positive feelings have not been shown to cause as much harm as negative feelings

100 but all feelings as long as they are kept in check will allow us to lead safer and more meaningful lives.

Do not let your anger control you.
1. Think before you speak.
2. Take a time out.
3. Identify possible solutions.
4. Try relaxation techniques such as deep breathing.
5. Be logical once you have calmed down.

Choose the correct answer and circle the correct letter.

1 Based on the information in paragraph one, it can be assumed that _____.
   A   unfeeling people are irrational
   B   all situations result in different feelings
   C   ecstasy and utter despair are everyday feelings
   D   people see some feelings as more important than others

2 The main purpose of paragraph two is to _____.
   A   explain why certain moods are dominant
   B   identify dominant moods
   C   emphasize that it is normal for everyone to have a dominant mood
   D   state that positive and negative feelings are equally important

3 According to the author, people who experience dominant positive feelings might be able to _____.
   A   detach themselves from everyday situations
   B   turn usually annoying situations into positive ones
   C   forget all past irritations
   D   enjoy doing things that they did not enjoy previously

4 (a) In paragraph four, the author's opinion of happy feelings shows _____.
   A   the importance of happiness in everyone's lives
   B   that happiness cannot always be achieved
   C   that more people are feeling happier today than before
   D   the type of friends that people with happy feelings will have

(b) Give details from the paragraph to support the answer in part A.

_____

_____

_____

_____

_____

_____

_____

_____

_____

_____

_____

_____

_____

_____

5 Which of the following from paragraph five shows that the author expresses a different opinion about negative feelings compared to the earlier paragraph?

A "we should negate the negative emotions that we feel" (lines 37-38)

B "the result of minor inconveniences that we push to the back of our minds once the incident is over" (lines 43-45)

C "perfect driving force of our future actions" (line 47)

D "do not cause any drastic impact on how we lead the rest of our day" (lines 45 - 46)

6 Which of the feeling is not a way in which fear and anxiety can help us in our daily lives?

A To make better plans

B To consider consequences of actions

C To be conscientious

D To avoid all types of events

(7) "It is certainly not a weakness as some might see it but an emotion that can be turned into a strength for leading a more meaningful life." (lines 52-53)

How does the quote above affect the reader's understanding of negative feelings?

A   They are necessary in life.

B   They change all the time.

C   They should not be ignored all the time.

D   They are not felt by people who are weak.

(8) What is the main idea in paragraph seven?

A   Setbacks lead to improvements.

B   Motivation does not happen all the time.

C   Good jobs only come to those who are frustrated.

D   Negative feelings happen to both the young and old.

(9) The author states that anger is a feeling "people might try to suppress." (line 73) State his views for and against such behaviors. Support your answer with details from the passage.

In your response, state:

• the author's views of why such anger might need to be suppressed

• the author's view of why it is important that the anger is not suppressed

_____

_____

_____

_____

_____

_____

_____

_____

_____

_____

_____

_____

_____

10 (a) What does "by-product of anger" (lines 91-92) tell the reader about the relationship between anger and having a bad temper?

A   Not everyone who is angry has a bad temper.

B   It is inevitable that anger will lead to bad tempers.

C   Having a bad temper shows that a person is extremely angry.

D   A bad temper does not stem from anger.

(b) What relevance does the text in the box have on the answer in Part A?

A   Everyone must be good tempered.

B   Anger should be suppressed at all times.

C   It is important that angry people seek professional help.

D   Anger management is an important skill that everyone should have.

Glossary

gamut: the complete range of something
He was able to gain a gamut of experience from his new job.

exacerbating: to make something worse
By telling them your opinion, you merely exacerbated the problem instead of solving it.

accosted: to be spoken to in a threatening way
She was accosted on her way home from school by a man in a trenchcoat.

suppressed: to stop oneself from showing one's feelings
She tried to suppress her feelings about the matter as she did not want to add fuel to fire.

dissipate: to become weaker than before
His anger dissipated the moment she apologized.

buzzword: a word or a phrase that is important at this point in time.
What is the buzzword in the computer industry today?

EXERCISE 3

/12
points

Read the passage carefully.

Leaving Home

When I was a young boy, having just entered teenhood, I lived in the town of Marscapone with a handful of newly built high rise apartment blocks and a single office tower. Urbanization came slightly later to the town compared to the surrounding towns. The buildings were interspersed with palm trees. Two rows
5 of palm trees stood on either side along the newly created cobblestone path that led to the sea. I loved Marscapone. It was unlike the other towns in the area. Here, there were vestiges of urbanization within the rustic charm of a quaint old town. Urbanization would never wield its ugly hands over the town.

Most of the townspeople were still farmers and my family was one of them.
10 Even though my brother left the drab sprawling farmhouse we lived in to work in the glitzy, confined office tower, he was the one who stuck out like a sore thumb. We were satisfied that the income we obtained from selling our crops and farm produce allowed us to purchase some modern amenities like a flat screen television, a microwave oven and cellphone that we shared among ourselves.

15 When he first started work, my brother would leave home before the sun rose and take the lone bus that plied along the dirt road a mile from our farm. Every evening, by the time he came home from work, we would have finished dinner and he would eat alone, watching television. Initially, he told us about his day at work. However, after a while, he found it hard to explain why life in the city was
20 so much more exciting than life back on our farm and so he said little to us. Several quarrels broke out between my parents and my brother, ending with my brother storming off to his room, yelling that my parents were old-fashioned and too set in their ways. I suppressed my interest in learning more and never asked my brother about his work.

25 I suspected that my brother would ask to move out of the house soon and live in one of the high rise apartment blocks near his workplace. There was nothing for him to look forward to at home and for a person who hated traveling long distances, the commute must have been especially exhausting and dull to him. Half a year

later, my brother announced at breakfast one Sunday that he was moving to an apartment just a few blocks away from his office. "I will not have to wake up so early and I will be able to sleep earlier at night as well." I could not help chuckling when I heard his reason. Of late, he had been avoiding my parents who were grumbling incessantly about mundane things, as my brother called them, the insects that had viciously attacked the crops and the poor quality of milk produced by the cows. Their friends had children who helped them on the farm and thought of ways to improve yields. My brother would never help them, for he wanted them to sell the farm and move to the city; but my parents were proud of the farm. They never failed to remind us of how they had brought us up with just whatever they had on the farm and although the effects of their words on me were like water off a duck's back, my brother seemed particularly annoyed by what they said. When he spoke of his colleagues' parents who lived in the city, my parents turned up their noses at them, scoffing at them for not being able to make real contributions to the country. "Who would feed the people then if everyone were like them?"

When my brother moved out of the house the following Saturday, my father busied himself with the crops, muttering about an attack from a swarm of insects the night before. My mother kept the machine in the kitchen on at full speed, churning out batter for cookies that she said she was going to start selling at the market. As I walked out with my brother, it was clear that he would see us less once he left home. Perhaps, we would only see him on weekends or on special occasions. Perhaps, he would insist that we visit him instead. I helped my brother to take his things to a waiting taxi. I noticed my father turn to gaze at us, his shoulder hunched before a small plot of green leaves. When we were younger, he would have berated us for doing things that he did not approve of; but now that we were older, he never imposed his ideas on us the way he had done before. Nagging was his way of hinting at what he wanted. When that didn't get through, he would just withdraw, the way he was now. "Avoidance. Don't you just hate that? Can't he be a man and face up to things especially those he apparently dislikes?" my brother mumbled as he lifted a heavy suitcase into the taxi. I shrugged, trying to ignore the pain I felt for my father. Perhaps, I wasn't supposed to feel that. After all, I was supposed to be on my brother's side right? We were brothers and we stood as one – our parents always told us that.

Before leaving, he pressed a bundle of money in my palm and told me to visit him when I was free. He would show me the city and he was certain that I would like it. "Leave mom and dad on the farm then if they want to be obstinate. It might be the only way for them to finally come to their senses." I just smiled at him and nodded. I knew that he was right; but I too had developed a sense of attachment

to the farm and I had an affinity with the animals, something that I was too afraid to tell my brother. I wanted him to approve of what I did as much as I was afraid to anger my parents. I figured that I could ride out this dilemma I was in for a few
70 more years until I finished school and was supposed to contribute to the family income. By then, perhaps urbanization would overwhelm the town and my parents would see the benefits of city living. It would then make sense for me to leave the farm. However, it could be the other way around - urbanization might never reach the farm, perhaps, and those modern buildings with their shiny exterior would
75 start to corrode. I was only in my teens. I could wait to see what the town had in store for me.

Choose the correct answer and circle the correct letter.

1 "Urbanization would never wield its ugly hands over the town." (line 8) Which of the following supports this idea?

- A "The buildings were interspersed with palm trees." (line 4)
- B "Here, there were vestiges of urbanization within the rustic charm of a quaint old town." (lines 6-7)
- C "Urbanization came slightly later to the town compared to the surrounding towns." (lines 3-4)
- D "Two rows of palm trees stood on either side along the newly created cobblestone path that led to the sea." (lines 4-6)

2 The author felt that his brother "stuck out like a sore thumb." (line 11) The author uses this simile to emphasize that _____.

- A the people did not care much about working in an office
- B living on a farm was more pleasant than living in the city area
- C people who moved from the farm to an office behaved differently
- D working in an office brought in more money than working on a farm

3 (a) What is the main idea the author tries to convey in paragraph 3?

- A The author's brother did not enjoy being with his family.
- B The family wished they could spend more time with the author's brother.
- C The distance between the author's brother and the rest of the family was increasing.
- D Problems happened because the author's brother no longer cared about his family.

(b) Explain your answer in Part A. Give one detail from the paragraph that supports your answer.

_____

_____

_____

_____

_____

_____

_____

_____

_____

_____

_____

_____

_____

_____

4 "Who would feed the people then if everyone were like them?" (line 43)
This showed that the author's parents _____.
A   were traditional people
B   were passionate about farming
C   were proud about what they did
D   were not comfortable with change

5 "Their friends had children who helped them on the farm and thought of ways to improve yields." (lines 35-36)
How does this further our understanding of the author's family?
A   The author's parents did not want to be left alone to work on the farm.
B   The author wanted to stay on the farm to keep his parents happy.
C   The author's parents tolerated their children's disobedience.
D   The author wanted to be like the children in the other families.

6　What is the main purpose of the phrase "effects of their words on me were like water off a duck's back" (lines 39-40)?

A　Explain why the author did not like his life

B　Describe the type of life the author was leading

C　Portray obstacles that the author would face in future

D　Contrast the different personalities of the author and his brother

7　(a)　How did the author convey his parents' emotions about his brother leaving the house?

A　He described their actions on the morning his brother left.

B　He explained why they were feeling upset.

C　He stated the conversation he had with his brother.

D　He highlighted his brother's irritation with his parents.

(b)　How did the parents feel when the author's brother left? Support your answer with your response in Part A and details from the passage.

_____

_____

_____

_____

_____

_____

_____

_____

_____

_____

_____

_____

_____

_____

_____

_____

8 (a) Which of the following from the passage best explains what the author's brother thought of their parents?

   A   "benefits of city living" (line 72)
   B   "come to their senses" (line 65)
   C   "grumbling incessantly about mundane things" (lines 32-33)
   D   "face up to things especially those he apparently dislikes" (line 57)

   (b) Explain your response in Part A.

   _____

   _____

   _____

   _____

   _____

   _____

   _____

   _____

   _____

   _____

   _____

   _____

   _____

   _____

   _____

9 What effect does the author create by ending the story with "I could wait and see what the town had in store for me"?

   A   Definite conclusion to the story
   B   Increased confusion among the characters
   C   Uncertain of what might happen in the future
   D   Heightened tension between the author and his brother

10 The internal conflict within the author is demonstrated by both his actions and his thoughts. Explain what impact this conflict will have on his family. Support your answer with details from the passage.

_____

_____

_____

_____

_____

_____

_____

_____

_____

_____

_____

_____

_____

Glossary

drab: not bright; dull
The house was painted a drab green.

sprawling: to be spread over a large area
They lived in a sprawling house in the suburbs.

glitzy: glamorous
She enjoyed attending glitzy parties hosted by the rich and famous.

confined: to be restricted in a particular place
The princess did not like to be confined in her room and often begged to be let out to the garden to play.

mundane: ordinary and uninteresting
She found her job mundane and wanted to look for a new one.

affinity: to have a strong feeling of understanding towards someone or something
George enjoys working at the dog shelter because he has an affinity for the dogs there.

corrode: to be slowly destroyed due to water, chemicals or other substances
When we renovated the house, we had to change the water pipes as they had corroded.

BASIC

EXERCISE 4

/12
points

Read the passage carefully.

Food and Cooking

Food refers to a substance that we need to keep ourselves alive. It provides us with the energy we need to carry out our daily activities and the nutrition we need to stay healthy. From the time of ancient civilization until now, food has always been an integral part of everyone's life. In each period, studies have always
5   been done on the different aspects of food. Whether it is the way food is obtained and prepared to the value of food and how food is distributed, there is always a tremendous amount of interest in food. Today, the study of food continues to appeal to researchers. Consumers devour all the information presented to them, using it to make decisions on food in their daily lives.

10 Food related advertisements dominate us, snaking their way into every aspect of our lives. Even if we pay no attention to food other than for it to fulfill our basic need of survival, it will be impossible to ignore all the advertisements that scream "Buy us" or "Use us" whether on screen or paper. Consequently, what these advertisements want to convey is that our lives can only get better if we make these
15 items part of our daily activities. We are confronted with billboards looming up at us from the side of the roads. They cannot be missed, not just because of their size but also because of the array of brilliant colors. At night, the billboards light up, creating an almost festive mood with their flashing neon lights. Some of the more creative ones have 3D images of their food items jutting out from the billboards.
20 One of the most common food related billboards is fast food. From hamburgers, to pizzas and hotdogs, these billboards remind everyone that there is delicious food waiting at these restaurants for their consumption. Often, they are accompanied by words like "juicy and tender," "100% prime cut beef used," among many others. All these serve to whet people's appetite and encourage them to stop for a meal at
25 the restaurants. Even if billboards do not do enough to motivate us to eat at those restaurants, there are also flyers that are distributed, telling people about a newly opened restaurant or a restaurant offering a discount on a special deal. Turn on the Internet and there are advertisements at the side of the webpage we are visiting. Advertisements for food are everywhere and in every form.

30   What does this mean for the food industry? It shows the wide variety of choices that people have when it comes to meal selection. In ancient societies, the food eaten was what could be obtained from a day of hunting in the forest or what was harvested from the people's own plots of land. There was little in terms of variety and sometimes, food was insufficient for everyone in the family. Once

35   supply began surpassing demand, there was a need for each food producer to be better than others. Getting more people to buy their food instead of others became important and competition began. From lower prices to attractive food packages, food producers have tried innovative ways to attract consumers. Today, there are choices to be made for every meal we eat. Being just average is not enough to oust

40   the competition in practically every type of cuisine. In any one street, there could be more than one Italian restaurant, Chinese restaurant or Mexican restaurant. The more ingenious ones who came up with fusion food now find themselves wrestling with a large number of restaurants serving similar food as well. With such stiff competition, restaurants now allocate more money to advertising to outdo their

45   competition and gain more customers. Competition is so heated that samples are also given out to entice people to visit the restaurant and hopefully feel that the food served there delights their taste buds.

        However, the attention given to food is not just on the number of restaurants available today. Although people have more choices outside the home and can spend

50   less time cooking at home, just as much attention is given to food that is cooked at home. The focus here is about creating greater convenience and efficiency when it comes to cooking at home. "You can make the most mouthwatering dishes with this latest blender!" How many times have such advertisements been heard shouting out to people from the television screens? There are also programs dedicated to

55   the advertising of kitchen equipment with viewers being able to purchase these advertised items with just a phone call or the click of a button. Such equipment promises to make cooking at home fuss free. Cooking at home with this new specialized equipment will be:

        • Simple
60   • Healthy
        • Quick
    The equipment is:
        • Not bulky
        • Easy to store
65   • Easy to clean

        The preponderance of such kitchen equipment today does not necessarily indicate that large numbers of people are still cooking their meals at home. With a more hectic lifestyle and the ease at which food can be obtained outside the home, fewer people are cooking their meals at home. Yet, such equipment will make it suitable for those who continue to remain devoted to homecooked meals, to those who are ambivalent about homecooked meals and to those who have yet to throw in the towel to homecooked meals but might do so soon if they are not given the help that they need.

Whether it is advertisements to entice people to visit restaurants, to purchase certain types of food or to buy particular kitchen equipment, food is being taken out of the domain of individual homes and into the public arena. Cooking is no longer done within the confines of one's own family or within a group of close friends. Cooking shows are also no longer just about presenting a particular recipe to the audience. Cooking has become a spectator sport. It has become competitive. Even if the program is about how particular dishes are cooked, the main objective is to entertain and not to teach specific skills and techniques. Often celebrity chefs are the ones hosting the programs. Most of the dishes are just too spectacular for regular homecooked dishes. Often, tedious aspects of the cooking process are excluded, resulting in a program that makes cooking look effortless with ingredients magically chopped up beforehand and condiments arranged to create a kitchen that looks like the one in a restaurant yet within a homey environment. The number of reality cooking shows is also on the rise, receiving ratings that are just as high as regular sitcoms. These shows film people in cooking competitions, in their roles as amateur chefs and also where they try to perform amazing feats with ordinary food such as deserts to cater to their customers' needs. Ironically, as people cook less at home, their attention seems to be focused more on food programs. The more people watch food programs, the less time they want to spend in their own kitchen cooking a meal. If they have to, they will look to new and efficient equipment that will give them the luxury of cutting down on the tedious time spent in the kitchen.

What has caused the changing face of the food industry? Societal change and progress have become the driving force of this change. Movement from an agrarian society to a manufacturing one and thereafter to the focus on technology has led to changes in the way the food industry has developed and how it has been viewed. For example, when mass production of items became commonplace, the mass production of food also increased in popularity. Frozen food and canned food, among others, are produced in a factory. There is consistency in the food, price drops because of economies of scale and most importantly, consumption of food is convenient. With technology, food testing procedures become more complex and detailed, making food safer for consumption for all. Food preservation techniques also improved. Most importantly, technology has been used, as mentioned earlier, to make information about food more accessible and this has piqued people's interest in food, reaching a peak that has never before been achieved.

Choose the correct answer and circle the correct letter.

1. As used in paragraph one, the word "devour" (line 8) has the closest antonym in
   _____.

   A   reject
   B   accept
   C   concur
   D   grasp

2. The author states that it is "impossible to ignore all the advertisements." (line 12) Which of the following is not a way in which advertisers attract people's attention?

   A   Size
   B   Color
   C   Creativity
   D   Ingredients

3. (a) How does the phrase "snaking their way" (line 10) affect the reader's understanding of the impact of advertisements on food?

   A   There are too many advertisements on food today.
   B   Advertisements on food are harmful to consumers.
   C   Consumers cannot avoid advertisements on food.
   D   Advertisements on food are everywhere but are hardly noticed.

   (b) Explain using the answer in Part A and details from the paragraph, why the author feels that way about advertisements for food.

   _____

   _____

   _____

   _____

   _____

   _____

   _____

   _____

   _____

   _____

4. How has the evolution of society led to greater choices for consumers?
   A   Progress allows the availability of food to exceed the need for it.
   B   Consumers are more open to trying new food as society evolves.
   C   More people are willing to produce food so supply of food increases.
   D   Technology allows people to be more aware of the types of food available.

5. What is the main idea the author wants to convey to the reader in paragraph three?
   A   The change in the way food is produced
   B   The impact of having more food choices on consumers
   C   The availability of a wide variety of restaurants everywhere
   D   The reasons competition is good for the food industry

6. The author emphasizes the need for "convenience" and "efficiency" (line 51) when it comes to cooking at home. Explain how this need has affected the food industry. Support your answer with details from the passage.

_____

_____

_____

_____

_____

_____

_____

_____

_____

_____

_____

_____

7. What effect do the features given in points in the passage have on the reader's understanding of cooking today?
   A   Emphasizes how easy it is to cook
   B   States that only new kitchen equipment can be used
   C   Contrasts old and new types of kitchen equipment
   D   Shows the wide variety of food that can be cooked

8   What importance does the author place on kitchen equipment today?

     A   Can be used by everyone

     B   Is necessary in every household

     C   Still necessary for particular groups of people

     D   Will reduce the number of people who eat outside the home

9   The author states that "Ironically, as people cook less at home, their attention seems to be focused more on food programs." (lines 90-91)

     Which of the following is not a reason the author gives for such behavior?

     A   Cooking shows are exciting to watch.

     B   Well known chefs helm the programs.

     C   Tedious aspects of cooking are avoided.

     D   Special methods of cooking dishes are revealed.

10   Which of the following best summarizes the author's argument about the food industry today?

     A   Food in the past is better than it is today.

     B   People's relationship with food changes as society changes.

     C   The more food programs there are, the less people care about food.

     D   It is important to prevent the food industry from undergoing numerous changes.

Glossary

integral: a necessary part of something
    Are group discussions an integral part of the planning process?

confronted: to be faced with something
    She was confronted by a myriad of questions from the reporters the moment she emerged from her house.

surpassing: to be more than or better than
    His results surpassed our expectations

entice: to persuade someone to do something
    Many people entered the new boutique because they were enticed by the colorful clothes on display.

preponderance: to have more of something in a certain group compared to others
    There is a preponderance of males in some occupations compared to females.

ambivalent: to be unsure of whether one likes or dislikes something
    Most of the employees were ambivalent about the new company policies.

piqued (one's) interest: to feel interested in someone or something
    When I found out that my new neighbor used to work at the zoo, my interest was piqued and I decided to get to know him.

Sadlier School

BASIC

EXERCISE 5

/12
points

Read the passage carefully.

Businesses Today

Businesses today are not just about making profits. There are many other aspects of businesses that might even add to their costs. Yet, these are regarded by some businesses as compulsory practices. There are three areas that businesses today focus on, of which making profits is not the main purpose. They are environment,
5   philanthropy, and ethical labor practices.

Naturally, the environment is a significant concern of many businesses today. Businesses both large and small have a large carbon footprint. This ranges from smaller issues such as paper usage in their everyday operations, to issues with more detrimental effects such as industrial carbon emissions. There are numerous
10   ways for businesses to reduce carbon emissions. Hence, any efforts to reduce those footprints are both favorable for the company and the society as a whole. There are direct benefits to society with the reduction of a company's carbon footprint but there are also clear benefits to the company itself. Regardless of the main reason for a company's move to "go green", in doing so, the company inadvertently looks for
15   more effective ways to reduce its own costs. When costs are reduced, the company also tends to be more environmentally friendly. For example, Google, a household name, prides itself on being able to reduce its carbon footprint to zero. One might think that Google will not be using much paper since its focus is on the Internet; but the data centers and offices around the world require energy in order to run.
20   Google, therefore, ensures that the centers are energy efficient, using renewable energy whenever possible. The use of renewable energy has reduced Google energy usage at data centers to about half of a typical data center. To further ensure that it is contributing to the environment, Google invests in companies that engage in renewable energy projects. This will help to keep the earth clean.

25   There are other ways in which a company's carbon footprint can be reduced. For example, Starbucks' "Toward 100% recycling" project might impress and entice socially aware customers to patronize them instead of another coffee joint despite steeper prices. With the expansion of the Louis Vuitton brand and its business, it

has also been actively putting in effort to reduce their carbon footprint. They now
ship more than 50% of their goods via ship rather than air to reduce greenhouse
emissions and they also run campaigns whereby they donate a percentage of sales
to 'The Climate Project'. Saving the environment has indeed led to dual results at
a time when environmental concerns are becoming widespread.

Philanthropy is another area of focus for businesses. There are many big and
small charitable organizations that can benefit from the philanthropic actions of
businesses. Despite the lack of laws, businesses contribute voluntarily to charitable
organizations. Who would have thought that altruistic behaviors would arise from
those whose main aim was to increase profits and reduce costs? Walmart, the well
known retail giant, has consistently contributed a portion of its profits to charitable
organizations. Besides Walmart, Chevron Corporation also looks to increase its
contributions to charitable organizations every year. These businesses and many
more are willing to help these organizations because it is a mission that they have
set out to accomplish. They want to help the communities so that people can lead
better lives. However, companies are looking for more innovative ways to help
the community. Besides cash donations, non-cash ways of helping the community
are on the rise. For example, some companies are giving away a portion of their
products to charitable organizations. By way of illustration, Baxter, a leader in
healthcare, contributes to charitable organizations through a range of cash and
non-cash giving. In 2009, Baxter donations helped improve living conditions and
healthcare for abandoned children in Mexico. Baxter also donates its products to
charity. In 2009, Baxter donated its products to 76 countries in need. Tablets that
can purify contaminated water are especially welcomed in the aftermath of a flood.
Antibiotics and other medicine are also donated to help victims of natural disasters.
Employees also spend many hours helping out at hospitals, community park clean-
up days and even teaching at local schools. As a healthcare corporation, Baxter is in
the best position to provide the medical care that the needy require but do not have
the means to obtain. Without the help of healthcare companies like Baxter, both the
needy and victims of natural disasters will not be able to obtain the medicine and
medical supplies that they need.

This arm of businesses is sometimes very important to the mission of the
company because it has become the best way to find the top candidates from among
those who have newly graduated. For example, General Electric has made a name
for itself on the philanthropic front and this has helped them to attract many young
and talented people to the company. The young adults realize the importance of
caring for the community and are attracted to companies that show they are doing
their part for the community.

Besides going beyond the company to lend a helping hand to those in need, company rules and regulations are also important. Ethical labor practices must exist in the company. Companies care for their employees in several ways. One way in
70 which this is done is to ensure that wages are fair. When employees are paid well, they are more motivated to work and feel less frustrated about dull and tedious jobs.

Some companies go beyond just fair wages but also ensure that their employees have a comfortable working environment. Ensuring that employees are happy will allow companies to retain these employees. Some companines ensure that
75 they have good training programs for their employees. Some of these programs help new employees to adjust to their jobs, making them feel less frustrated about learning the ropes. There are companies also who create a favorable environment for their employees. This perhaps, is one of the most important ways to improve employee welfare, surpassing even that of increased wages. For example at Google,
80 the emphasis is to create a conducive environment that encourages innovation and productivity. Hence, from outdoor terraces with chaises to theme-based dining areas, employees have ample places to either engage in discussion with their colleagues or to sit quietly with a book.

Employees, especially those with family commitments, also favor companies
85 where the working arrangements are flexible. As long as the work permits, some employees are allowed to work from home or go to the office at a convenient time. What is important is that the arrangement allows them to improve their productivity which will eventually bring benefits to the company. Some employees look for a healthy work environment. This includes healthcare programs that workers
90 can benefit from such as providing healthcare screening. For example, Cheveron Corporation encourages its employees to complete an assessment that will measure employees' chances of suffering from cardiovascular illnesses. Talks on excessive stress, poor nutrition, obesity, among others alert employees to the importance of leading a healthy lifestyle. The company hopes to influence the way employees lead
95 their lives, leading to long term lifestyle changes. Keeping employees healthy will, therefore, also encourage productivity and increase workplace safety.

There are more aspects of businesses than increasing profits. Businesses today are concerned about the welfare of their workers, the community they are living in and the wider community. However, in the long run, these concerns have a positive
100 impact on the businesses as well, giving them opportunities to develop. There is also financial gain that for some businesses, was never the original intention.

Choose the correct answer and circle the correct letter.

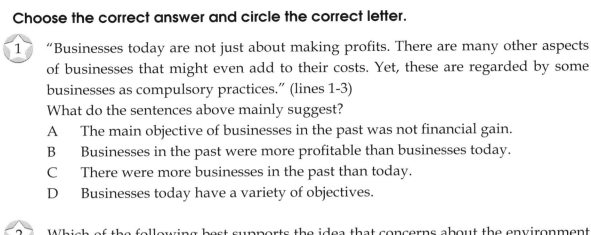

1. "Businesses today are not just about making profits. There are many other aspects of businesses that might even add to their costs. Yet, these are regarded by some businesses as compulsory practices." (lines 1-3)

   What do the sentences above mainly suggest?

   A   The main objective of businesses in the past was not financial gain.

   B   Businesses in the past were more profitable than businesses today.

   C   There were more businesses in the past than today.

   D   Businesses today have a variety of objectives.

2. Which of the following best supports the idea that concerns about the environment are very important?

   A   "Naturally, the environment is a significant concern of many businesses today." (line 6)

   B   "Businesses both large and small have a large carbon footprint." (line 7)

   C   "Hence, any efforts to reduce those footprints are both favorable for the company and the society as a whole." (lines 10-11)

   D   "There are numerous ways for businesses to reduce carbon emissions." (line 9- 10)

3. The author uses Google as an example of how a business has reduced its carbon footprint. Explain why this example best shows that environmental concerns are important to businesses today. Support your answer with details from the passage.

   _____

   _____

   _____

   _____

   _____

   _____

   _____

   _____

   _____

   _____

   _____

Sadlier School

4. How does the example of Starbucks develop the reader's understanding of environmental awareness today?

A   It is simply to protect the environment.

B   It is of utmost importance for many people.

C   It is only practiced by well known businesses.

D   It is created by people who own businesses.

5. The author states that "Who would have thought that altruistic behaviors would arise from those whose main aim was to increase profits and reduce costs," (lines 37-38) to show _____.

A   that businesses are actually set up to earn profits

B   that businesses are only about being kind to the needy

C   that businesses can only make financial gains in one way

D   that it is possible to help the needy and earn profits simultaneously

6. The author states that philanthropic behavior takes place even though they do not bring in profits for the businesses. Explain the author's reason for philanthropic behavior. Support your answer with details from the passage.

_____

_____

_____

_____

_____

_____

_____

_____

_____

_____

_____

_____

_____

_____

_____

7   What is the main objective of paragraph 5 in the understanding of philanthropic behavior of companies?
    A   It consists of many young employees.
    B   It is the best way to hire a large number of new employees.
    C   It could result in long term financial gain for the companies.
    D   It is a necessary progression for companies that have been around for a long time.

8   Read paragraph 6. What is the meaning of the word "ethical" (line 68) used in the paragraph?
    A   New and improved
    B   Important and widespread
    C   Correct and unbiased
    D   Beneficial and innovative

9   The author states that companies go "beyond just fair wages" today. (line 72) What does this reveal to the reader about the different ways companies retain their employees?
    A   Good wages are the traditional way of retaining employees.
    B   A raise in wages are given if the employee deserves it
    C   It is important for wages to increase every year.
    D   There are many effective ways to retain employees.

10 (a)   "Companies care for their employees in several ways." (line 69) What is the main conclusion we can draw from this?
          A   The amount spent on employees must continually increase.
          B   A conducive working environment is important for employees.
          C   Employees will only work if they are satisfied with their environment.
          D   All companies should think of numerous ways to care for their employees.

(b) The author describes how companies care for their employees. Explain why these are effective ways of caring for employees. In your response, use evidence from the passage to
- identify the different ways
- contrast these ways

_____

_____

_____

_____

_____

_____

_____

_____

_____

_____

_____

_____

_____

_____

_____

_____

_____

Glossary

inadvertently: without realizing something
  She inadvertently sent a virus to all her friends in her address book when she opened the attachment in the email.

entice: to persuade someone to do something by offering the person something attractive
  Many people were enticed by the discounts offered at the new supermarket.

altruistic: to show concern for others even without obtaining any advantage to doing that
  His actions to help the needy in his community are purely altruistic.

Sadlier School

DATE: .... NAME: ....

CLASS: ....

EXERCISE 6

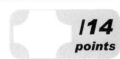

/14
points

Read the passage carefully.

Social Media and Our Brains

Technology as we know it is evolving at breakneck speed and is a far cry from the 1980s and 1990s where Internet connectivity was carried out through dial-up; websites then loaded at speeds that would now be considered snail's pace and online banking and shopping were but wisps of dreams that did not yet exist. The

5 development of technology and better Internet connectivity has led to the advent of social media.Social media is defined as computer related tools that allow people to create, share and exchange information, ideas, pictures and videos within virtual communities and networks. Such exchanges take place on an unprecedented scale today on a daily basis, surpassing other forms of interaction and communication.

10 Even though the first social media site appeared less than twenty years ago, social media usage has surged tremendously to include approximately one-third of the world's population. Today, Facebook is the largest social networking site, with its online population making it the third largest population in the world behind the physical populations of India and China. Other popular social media networks

15 include Twitter, Instagram, LinkedIn and Pinterest. Social media now influences areas that many never dreamed of in the past. From making new friends to learning about events around the world right when they occur, social media has become part and parcel of our lives. There is unequivocal proof that social media has changed the course of history and dramatically altered the way we interact with one another.

20 What has emerged recently, however, is that social media may also have lasting influences on our brains and the way that they are wired.

Mobile device ownership is at an all-time high, with some polls suggesting that there are more people in the world who own a mobile device than a toothbrush. Social media is after all only a click away, at our fingertips and in our pockets, any

25 time of the day. As a result, the prevalence of Internet addictions has also increased, with between five to ten percent of Internet users unable to control the amount of time spent online. A large proportion of Internet usage is often associated with social media use. Brain scans of heavy Internet users show a degradation of white matter in the brain, especially in areas that control attention, emotional processing and

decision-making. Some effects of these may include poorer decision-making skills and self-control, and shortened attention spans, among others. These impairments suggest that heavy Internet use may have neurological effects. This is in spite of the fact that it is considered a psychological addiction, not simply a physical one.

Dopamine is a chemical released by the brain. It is involved in sending signals to other nerve cells and plays a major role in reward-motivated behavior; carrying out rewarding activities increases the level of dopamine in our brains, causing us to feel good. This in turn makes us more likely to repeat the rewarding behavior. Dopamine levels rise when we exercise, get sufficient sleep and accomplish goals we set for ourselves, which might explain the natural "feel good" rush that sets in when we engage in such activities. Social media usage can be considered a pleasurable activity that boosts our dopamine levels. As in the case of many addictions, our brains develop increased tolerance to dopamine over time and we may unknowingly be spending more time using social media in order to obtain the same good feelings that we used to.

In considering social interaction, dopamine levels have shown a greater spike when we talk about ourselves as compared to talking about others. Traditionally, 30 to 40 percent of face to face communication involves talking about our own experiences. In contrast, 80 percent of social media use revolves around us, and not the other. With increasing amounts of interaction taking place online, our bodies may actually be rewarding us for talking about ourselves. Each time a friend "likes" something we post online, or posts a comment online about something we said, we not only receive a notification online, but also a boost in our dopamine levels. Not everyone responds equally, however, and studies have been able to distinguish the heavy Internet users from the light Internet users by studying the spike in the levels of dopamine in response to such notifications online.

Many of us consider ourselves to be excellent at multi-tasking or carrying out multiple activities simultaneously like the way the computer has been created to function. We pride ourselves at being able to reply to a text message, have a meal, watch television, check our Facebook page and carry out a conversation with a friend, all at the same time. While it might be easy to believe that social media has improved our ability to multi-task, research suggests otherwise. Research participants were tested on their ability to switch successfully between different tasks and results showed that heavy social media users performed significantly worse than others on these tests. Heavy social media usage may alter our brains to make it harder for our brains to commit information to memory and filter out extraneous material, thus impairing the ability to carry out particular tasks successfully.

In 2003, the term "Phantom Vibration Syndrome" was first coined. Also known as Phantom Ringing Syndrome, it is a phenomenon that occurs when mobile phone users mistakenly perceive a vibration from their devices when there is none.

70 These vibrations are often physical itches that the brain has learned to interpret as a vibration of a mobile device. Nine in ten of participants studied reported experiencing Phantom Vibration Syndrome at least once every two weeks. While more research needs to be carried out in this area, researchers are startled by the way the increase in social media use and the prevalence of mobile devices seems to

75 be re-wiring our brains and triggering them in ways that have not been seen before. While Phantom Vibration Syndrome may not significantly impair one's day-to-day functioning, Dr. Larry Rosen, a research psychologist who studies technology and its effect on our minds, recommends taking a break from technology once in a while in order to reduce its effects on our minds. Such breaks need not be long stretches

80 of time and can range from 30 minutes to an hour at a time.

Having realized the negative effects social media has on our brains, it may be tempting to go cold turkey. However, all is not doom and gloom. It is worth noting that while current research suggests that social media can potentially impair our cognitive functions, most research to date has focused on heavy users

85 of social media, as opposed to light to moderate users. At best, these findings serve to provide greater awareness of the effects our online activities may have on our brains and highlight the need for moderation of usage as the risk of developing an over dependence on the Internet is a very real one; 53 percent of participants polled in a study said that they would rather lose their sense of smell than their

90 access to technology. There is no doubt that social media has allowed for a more fluid exchange of ideas between people and brought the world to our fingertips. It has also improved the way we network and socialize, with virtual communities and interest groups easily available online. An increasing number of organizations are making their presence felt on social media and have broken down the invisible

95 wall that stands between them and their consumers. The negative effects of social media must be weighed against its benefits. At the end of the day, moderation and well-regulated use are key, because social media has made its mark and is here to stay. In the words of Erik Qualman, an influential author and leading presence on social media, "We don't have a choice on whether we do social media…the choice

100 is how well we do it."

Choose the correct answer and circle the correct letter.

 1 "Even though the first social media site appeared less than twenty years ago, social media usage has surged tremendously to include approximately one-third of the world's population." (lines 10-12)

What does the sentence above mainly suggest?

A That technology is a global phenomenon

B That more people should be on social media

C That social media should have started a long time ago

D That technology will always play an important role in people's lives

 2 (a) The author states that social media is "part and parcel of our lives." (lines 17-18) What does this tell the reader about the impact of social media today?

A The presence of social media improves everyone's mood.

B The influence of social media in our lives is unhealthy.

C It is necessary for us to use social media in our daily activities.

D Constant improvements will be made in everyone's lives.

(b) What is the author's view of the impact of social media today? Is the author's reasoning sound? Support your answer using details from the answer in Part A and details from paragraph one.

_____

_____

_____

_____

_____

_____

_____

_____

_____

_____

_____

_____

_____

Sadlier School

3 The author states that "Internet addictions have also increased." (line 25) What is the main reason for this?

   A   Convenience at which technology is available
   B   Interesting mobile devices that are sold everywhere
   C   The need to feel constantly satisfied
   D   Many popular devices that are dependent on technology

 4 Which of the following best supports the idea that Internet addiction has been proven and tested?

   A   "Social media is thus only a click away, at our fingertips and in our pockets, any time of the day." (lines 24-25)
   B   "Brain scans of heavy Internet users show a degradation of white matter in the brain, especially in areas that control attention, emotional processing and decision-making." (lines 28-30)
   C   "Traditionally, 30 to 40 percent of face to face communication involves talking about our own experiences. In contrast, 80 percent of social media use revolves around us, and not the other." (lines 46-49)
   D   "Today, Facebook is the largest social networking site, with its online population making it the third largest population in the world behind the physical populations of India and China." (lines 12-14)

5 Why does the author provide both data from studies and descriptions of everyday activities in the passage?

   A   To increase readability by making the information presented more interesting
   B   Substantiate claims and show relevance of information in the passage
   C   Create greater awareness of the impact of technology in people's lives today
   D   Remove any doubts that people might have about social media

 6 (a)   "Many of us consider ourselves to be excellent at multi-tasking or carrying out multiple activities simultaneously like the way the computer has been created to function." (lines 56-58)
        The author uses this simile to emphasize that people today

   A   enjoy using the computer
   B   want to be better than the computer
   C   prefer to do more things than in the past
   D   are concerned about speed and efficiency

(b)   Does the author agree with the statement in Part A? Explain the author's reasoning for his point of view. Support your answer with details from the passage.

_____

_____

_____

_____

_____

_____

_____

_____

_____

_____

_____

_____

_____

_____

_____

_____

_____

7 What is the purpose of paragraph 5 in the development of the topic presented in this passage?

A   Explain the increase in scientific studies on social media

B   Emphasize the excessive influence of technology in people's lives

C   Insert a humorous event to lighten the discussion of social media

D   Highlight the popularity of cellphones in the use of social media

8 What does the author use to show that people can make changes in their lifestyle?

A   Description of data collected from surveys

B   Quotations about social media by famous people

C   Listing of the most popular social media sites

D   Explanation of how to reduce the negative effects of technology

9 According to the author, going "cold turkey" (line 82) might be "doom and gloom." (line 82) This shows that social media _____.

    A   has an extensive impact on people's lives.

    B   has negative effects on people's lives

    C   has unexpected influence on people's lives

    D   has more disadvantages than disadvantages

10 The author ends the passage with a positive outlook on the impact of technology on everyone's lives. Explain how he does this. How convincing is his argument? Support your answer with details from the passage.

_____

_____

_____

_____

_____

_____

_____

_____

_____

_____

Glossary

breakneck speed: very fast
    The driver of the sports car was traveling at breakneck speed along the freeway.

surged: to move suddenly and quickly
    The cars surged forward once the lights at the intersection changed.

prevalence: to be common among a large group of people
    The prevalence of security cameras has made this neighborhood a lot safer than before.

impairing: to damage
    The accident impaired his hearing and he cannot hear very well now.

influential: to have the power to change the way things are or the way people think
    Who is the most influential person in your life?

INTERMEDIATE

EXERCISE 7

Read the passage carefully.

The Book

"Got some books to sell," he said. "Sci-fi and fantasy mainly. The guy in the bookshop round the corner said you might be interested." I could not restrain a smile. Whenever old Kowalski found himself beleaguered by students trying to unload their books on him for holiday money at the end of the summer term, he

5 always gave them my address, though he knew my tastes were specialized and my funds limited. I would invariably send them on their way unrewarded after examining their wares with forged interest. "Well, you've come to the right place," I said. "I am something of a collector, yes." I gestured behind me to the impressively sagging bookshelves lining my walls. "So what rarities do you have to offer me?"

10 He loosened the drawstring of the duffel bag he carried on his shoulder and emptied its contents onto the mat at my feet. Dog-eared paperbacks with garish covers and fanciful titles were everywhere for my inspection but my eyes fixed on a slim hardback still sporting its glossy white jacket, though somewhat stained and darkened by age, like a dinner guest at the wrong party. The dust flap bore

15 the title *Book of Ands* and below it in smaller print the author's name, George Lewis Berg. "What's this?" I asked, picking out the volume from the mass grave in which it lay half-buried and opening it at random. The page was filled with regularly spaced columns of the single word 'and'. I thumbed further ahead, then back to the beginning; each page was the same. "Seems to be some sort of parody?"

20 "This was a present from a girl I used to go out with. It's my name, you see. Well, Andy really, but everyone calls me And. I guess she thought it was funny."

Such curiosities always interested me. With feigned indifference, I enquired, "And how much are you asking for this supposed masterpiece?"

"I couldn't let it go for less than ten dollars. Sentimental value, you know."

25 I offered him half of what he asked for and he accepted. The transaction completed, I invited my visitor in for coffee. I did not receive many callers and thought it might be agreeable to pass an idle hour or two in bookish conversation. To this end, I tried to elicit from my guest his opinion of the American contribution

to fantasy literature. Unfortunately, he appeared singularly ill-informed about the
whole subject and when he had dribbled the last of his coffee, I invented an excuse
about a dental appointment and saw him to the door. There were so few these days
with whom one could talk about matters that mattered.

One such person, perhaps the only person among my circle of friends, was
Kowalski the bookseller, and the following morning, I paid him a visit.

"Anything to your liking?"

I didn't understand him at first.

"From that guy I sent round yesterday?" He had a playful gleam in his eyes.

"As a matter of fact, I did get one interesting item from him, yes. It was
something of a surprise. A very odd book. Ever heard of the name George Lewis
Berg?"

"Berg, Berg," he repeated. "Sounds familiar. So many Bergers and Burgesses
these days. But Berg, no, I don't think so. I'll look it up in the Encyclopedia of
Literary Biography."

He wandered off through the dusty stacks crammed with high quality art books
and slim volumes of verse. Some minutes later, he returned bearing a weighty folio-
sized book open on his arms, crooked at the spine like a sleeping child.

"Berg, George Lewis," he read, "1885 to 1949." He transferred the volume to
my arms and I took it to the window where the light was better. The entry consisted
of a two-column biography and a list of Berg's major works – some dozen novels
and collections of verse, none of which I had heard of. I learned that he had worked
for most of his life as a librarian, until failing eyesight forced him to retire. He had
then spent the last ten years of his life composing his magnum opus. After his death,
however, the only manuscript found in his possession was that which came to be
published as *Book of Ands*. Provision had been made in his will for his final work
to be privately printed should he die before completing it, and in the absence of
any other manuscript, and out of respect for the dead man's wishes, this was done,
thereby producing 'perhaps the most bizarre literary artifact in history'. Berg was
said to have suffered several bouts of mental instability in his youth, the implication
appearing to be that at the end of his life, his sanity must have finally deserted him.

I summarized all this for Kowalski and told him how I purchased a copy of the
Book of Ands from the student he had sent me the previous day.

"Sounds crazy. Why would anyone want to write a book like that? Where's
the pleasure in such a book?"

"Perhaps, well, perhaps he did write his magnum opus and then simply began
cutting it."

"What do you mean?"

"Well, look at the facts. He worked on his novel for ten years, supposedly. How
many 'ands' can you write in ten years? Enough to fill a whole shelf of books. Yet
after his death, it seems only a small bundle of pages was found, suggesting he may
have written them not long before he died. What did he do for the rest of the time?"

"Are you asking me or telling me?"

"I'm just guessing, but well, perhaps when he'd finished his novel he came
to see that any conventional work of fiction – any narrative composed of nouns,
verbs, adjectives of the author's choosing – any conventional prose style inevitably
limits the reader's imagination, forces him to accept the writer's version of events
rather than create his own. Perhaps he began by cutting the odd adjectives here and
there, as many writers do, and it grew into a passion, a style, or anti-style. Haven't
we always been advised by our teachers to read more to know more? Perhaps our
teachers were wrong after all. Perhaps all authors should be like Berg. He probably
cut so much of his original novel that in the end he only had one word left."

"And?"

"Well, perhaps he then threw the manuscript of the novel away and just kept
re-typing the word he'd saved, the only word that freed rather than limited the
reader's imagination. Perhaps if he'd lived another year the book would have been
a couple of thousand pages longer."

"Wait a minute, I don't understand. You mean he wanted the reader to sort of…"

"Complete the novel himself. Exactly. Supply his own nouns, verbs and
adjectives. The perfect collaborative enterprise between reader and writer."

"Sounds crazy," replied Kowalski. "Where's the pleasure in that? Would any
of the famous writers have written such a book?"

"Perhaps Berg would have regarded them as tyrants, dictators of literature."

He shook his head with an expression of pity. "We can't all be great poets,
you know. Some of us are content to sit at the feet of the masters and enjoy the
stories secondhand. Some of us have no wish to be writers; some of us are happy
as readers." He closed the cover of the encyclopedia and shuffled back with it into
the gloom at the rear of the shop. "If everyone wrote their own books," he called
over his shoulder, "what would become of the humble bookseller?"

Choose the correct answer and circle the correct letter.

1 What does the phrase 'forged interest' (line 7) suggest about the author's relationship with Kowalski?

A   He had a close relationship with Kowalski and he cared about him.

B   He looked down on Kowalski and thought he had a poor knowledge of books.

C   His contact with Kowalski was limited and only through the students who went to his shop.

D   He did not know Kowalski well and was unwilling to have regular communication with him.

2 "And how much are you asking for this supposed masterpiece?"

"I couldn't let it got for less than ten dollars. Sentimental value, you know."

(lines 23-24)

How do the views of the author and the student contribute to your understanding of what value the book had?

A   The cost of the book did not match its value.

B   The true value of the book was controversial.

C   The book had little value to those who did not know its contents.

D   The book paled in comparison to other popular books of its time.

3 How does the author's conversation with the student contribute to our overall understanding of the author's character?

A   The author hid his real thoughts about books behind sarcasm.

B   The author had great pride in his massive knowledge of books.

C   Humor was the author's way of deflecting an awkward situation.

D   The author found it important to keep his customers in suspense.

4 Which of the following is an important detail in a summary of lines 25-32?

A   The student could not wait to leave the bookstore.

B   The author did not have any other interest except books.

C   The author did not have the patience for people who were ignorant about literature.

D   It was expected of any student to have an opinion of American fantasy literature.

5 Why did the author alternate his thoughts about the book with Kowalski's responses?

A   To show a different side of the author to the reader

B   To show Kowalski's interest in the topic being discussed

C   To show that the author was truly interested in the book

D   To show that the author knew what he was talking about

6　Which of the sentences from the passage best supports the idea that the author was impressed by the book he had bought from the student?

A　"It was something of a surprise." (line 38-39)

B　"Such curiosities always interested me." (line 22)

C　"The perfect collaborative enterprise between reader and writer." (line 88)

D　"He had then spent the last ten years of his life composing his magnum opus." (line 51-52)

7　(a)　Kowalski showed 'an expression of pity' (line 92). Why did he feel pity?

A　Those who wrote were considered tyrants.

B　Not everyone will be able to enjoy good books.

C　His bookstore will eventually close down.

D　There will not be many books in bookstores.

(b)　Support your answer in Part A with one detail from the rest of the paragraph.

_____

_____

_____

_____

_____

_____

_____

_____

_____

_____

_____

_____

_____

_____

_____

8. Explain what the author means when he says that a writer of books "limits the reader's imagination." Give details from the paragraph to show how he supports his point of view.

_____

_____

_____

_____

_____

_____

_____

_____

_____

_____

9. Explain how the author was depicted as a literary expert. Give two details from the passage to support your answer.

_____

_____

_____

_____

_____

_____

_____

_____

_____

_____

10 To what extent were Kowalski and the author's perception of literary works different? Support your answer with details from the passage. In your response,

- identify Kowalski's and the author's view of the *Book of Ands*
- explain how each of them supported their point of view

_____

_____

_____

_____

_____

_____

_____

_____

_____

_____

_____

_____

_____

_____

_____

_____

_____

_____

_____

_____

_____

Glossary

beleaguered: to be surrounded by
The town was beleaguered with soldiers at dawn before any of the people were awake.

invariably: always
Whenever we ask him to meet us for a meal, invariably declined.

bout: short period of time when something happened
She suffered from a bout of flu at the beginning of the year.

EXERCISE 8

/14
points

Read the passage carefully.

The Power of Music

Music has fascinated people throughout the ages. Its ability to bring people together, and its potential to heal has both astounded and confounded. Many have tried to rationalize how music does what it does, and many have failed to come up with a concrete explanation. The mystery behind a simple melody affecting
5   the human mind has not been fully unraveled. Yet, throughout history, music has shown the power it wields over humans time and time again, and its force cannot be ignored.

For instance, when World War I first broke out in 1914, the soldiers who were fighting on both sides had hoped that they would be home to celebrate Christmas
10   that year. As the war dragged on for four more years, many soldiers on the front did not get home at all. However, on Christmas Eve of the first year of the war, one of the most unexpected events in history took place. The weather had abruptly turned cold, freezing the trenches where the soldiers were camped out, and the morale of both sides had taken a turn for the worse. British sentries who were on guard duty
15   reported to their commanding officers that small lights on the other side had been raised on poles or bayonets. The lights took on a different meaning that night. It turned out that on the German side, soldiers had begun lighting candles. Although these had made the German troops clearly visible on that cold dark night, the British soldiers held their fire. The British officers had seen through their binoculars that
20   some enemy troops were even holding Christmas trees over their heads. These had candles in their branches, and the message sent was clear. The Germans, who celebrated Christmas on the eve of December 25th, were unrestrainedly sending holiday greetings to the British, their enemy in the war.

After a period of silence, a few German soldiers could be heard singing a
25   Christmas carol. It soon picked up as other German soldiers along the line joined in the singing. The words were"Stille Nacht! Heilige Nacht!"Recognizing the familiar tune of "Silent Night, Holy Night", the British soldiers joined in and began

Sadlier School

singing earnestly in English. The impromptu singing defused hostilities as soldiers reminisced about their families back home. One by one, British and German soldiers
30   began laying down their weapons to venture into no-man's land separating the two sides. The number of soldiers on both sides who ventured out was so huge that their superior officers could not object even if they wanted to. An implicit truce erupted and peace broke out, albeit for those few moments on the cold warfront. Two warring sides had been brought together through recognizable items and a
35   familiar musical melody that brought out the spirit of Christmas.

Another example of the power of music can be found in the annals of even earlier history. Throughout history, man has constantly searched for ways and means to alleviate his aches and pains as he goes through his daily routines. Some of these ways ranged from traditional and modern medicinal methods, to the more religious
40   praying to deities or gods to ease the troubles they faced. Some even believed in the truly bizarre practices that would make the doctors of today cringe, such as hammering a nail into a tree to cure a headache and trepanning, which involved boring a small hole into the skull to expose the outer membrane of the brain. This practice was believed to alleviate pressure and treat health problems localized
45   within the head, though it was also thought to cure epilepsy, migraines, and mental disorders. Needless to say, people kept searching for less horrific methods to cure their ailments. Hence, many ancient cultures turned to the less invasive method of sound and music for healing. Pythagoras called it "music medicine." He believed that the sun, moon and planets all emitted their own unique hum based on their
50   orbital revolution and that the quality of life on Earth reflected the tenor of celestial sounds that were physically unnoticeable to the human ear. The idea of music as a healing tool became so popular that in the Middle Ages, the study of music became a mandatory part of a physician's education, allowing them to understand the importance of music in the healing process.

55   However, as with all medicine, the proof is in the pudding. Statistical data and supporting evidence need to be collected and analyzed, before we can truly discover what music can actually heal. And therein lies the problem. Music as a form of medicine appears to be still in its intangible form, with only eyewitness accounts and the testimonies of die-hard believers to support its medicinal claims.
60   One-off success stories also do not contribute to the credibility of music therapy.

Music therapy in itself is not as intangible as it seems, however. Recent theories put forth have reasoned that listening to music is healing due to the power of musical intervals. A musical interval is created when one note is played with

Sadlier School

another note. Either playing two notes together, or one after the other can create
this interval. When two notes are played together, the interval has a theoretically
stronger effect on the human mind and body. The frequencies of the two notes of
the interval create a mathematical ratio that may affect the body in different ways.
This coincides with how in the past, architects used the ratios found in the musical
intervals when building sacred buildings. Buildings that contained these ratios were
the most pleasing to the eye, and had an uplifting effect on human consciousness.
The philosopher Goethe even said that "sacred architecture is frozen music."

Another theory put forth in support of music as healing was that of using
sympathetic resonance. In 1974, Fabien Maman was working as a touring jazz
guitarist. While playing at a concert tour with his band in Japan, he noticed that
the audience did not clap at the end of each song. The silence after each piece
puzzled him at first, and he thought that the band was playing something that did
not appeal to the Japanese audience. However, they did clap, but only at the end
of the concert. Although it felt awkward at first, he began to expect and even enjoy
the silence between the songs.

In the silence, he could begin to slowly feel the effect that each piece of music
had on him, which was something that he had never done before. He also began
noticing that after each concert, he had more energy left. After three months of
touring Japan, it dawned on Maman that clapping in between songs actually ruined
some of the benefits of the music that he was playing. He started taking notice of
certain musical keys that had a stimulating effect on both the musicians and the
audience. He discovered that the same piece of music played in a different key or
at a different time of year had a different effect on the listening audience as well
as the musicians playing them. The imperceptible effects of music were profound.

In 1981 Maman met a senior researcher called Hélène Grimal at the National
Center for Scientific Research in Paris. Like Maman, she too was interested in the
effects of music on humans, particularly at a cellular level. Forging a friendship,
Maman and Grimal studied the effects of sound on cancer cells for the next one
and a half years. Within this time period, they decided to work in the University
of Jussieu in Paris for five nights a week, carrying out their experiments at night in
the biological research laboratories. They also had to wait for the subway system to
stop its service so that its vibrations would not adversely affect their experiments.
The inconvenience was nothing compared to their discovery. They experimented
with healthy blood cells, hemoglobin, and cancer cells.

Sadlier School

Maman and Grimal took photographs from a microscope and recorded the
100   effects of playing different instruments on the cancer cells. These instruments
included drums, guitars and even the human voice. They found that at sound
frequencies between 'A' at 440Hz and 'B' 493Hz, the cancer cells would break down
and their structure would be thrown into complete disarray. The healthy cells, on the
other hand, remained intact or became stronger. Although this research into music
105   therapy is still in its infancy, its potential to cure seems almost limitless. If, as Maman
believes, the human body is indeed made up of a collection of vibrations which is
covered by its surrounding material form, then it would be hardly surprising that
sound vibrations caused by music must have an effect, either for good or bad.

Still, even today, most of the research regarding music therapy is considered
110   controversial as opposed to revolutionary. There is skepticism surrounding this
subject matter, like any other uncharted medical territories. Unless this field receives
a major breakthrough and a consistent record of healing, it shall have to be content
with its place in the background of modern medicine.

Choose the correct answer and circle the correct letter.

1 Which of the following show the influence of music in people's lives?
   A   "mystery behind a simple melody affecting the human mind has not been fully
         unraveled" (lines 4-5)
   B   "power it wields over humans time and time again" (line 6)
   C   "fascinated people throughout the ages" (line 1)
   D   "have tried to rationalize how music does what it does" (lines 2-3)

2 How do paragraphs 2 and 3 further the reader's understanding of music?
   A   Music can bridge differences between people.
   B   There are different types of music.
   C   Music should be played in times of war.
   D   Everyone enjoys music.

3 "lights took on a different meaning that night" (line 16)
   What is the main significance of the lights to the understanding of the passage?
   A   The lights explained why a Christmas celebration was necessary.
   B   The German soldiers used lights to emphasize the importance of music.
   C   The lights symbolized warmth which complemented the music that was played.
   D   The British soldiers realized the importance of music because of the lights.

4 The author states that "Two warring sides had been brought together through recognizable items and a familiar musical melody that brought out the spirit of Christmas." (lines 34-35) Explain how the spirit of Christmas was brought about by the "familiar musical melody" (line 35) and the "recognizable items." (line 34) Support your answer with details from the passage.

_____

_____

_____

_____

_____

_____

_____

_____

5 The author states that "the study of music became a mandatory part of a physician's education, allowing them to understand the importance of music in the healing process" (lines 52-54).

(a) What does this statement mainly suggest?

    A   Music was important in everyone's lives.

    B   The effects of music could be analyzed and understood.

    C   All physicians had to have good knowledge of music.

    D   Physicians had to use music in order to heal their patients.

(b) How does the author contradict the answer in Part A? Support your answer with two details from the passage.

_____

_____

_____

_____

_____

_____

_____

6. What impression of music does the author create with the phrase "sacred architecture is frozen music" (line 71)?
   A Music exists in different forms.
   B Music extends its influence to people from all walks of life.
   C It is important to use music in artistic creations.
   D Buildings are places where music can be found.

7. Which of the following explains the purpose of the research conducted by Maman and Grimal?
   A Scientific analysis of how body cells mutate with music
   B Specific study on the use of music to create body cells
   C Experiments on the effects of music on common illnesses
   D Extensive study on music therapy and cell creation

8. Which of the following is the best explanation of Pythagoras' description of music?
   A The state of a person's health is controlled by the sounds from movements in space.
   B The state of a person's health is unpredictable.
   C The changes in a person's health are not easily noticeable.
   D The changes in a person's health cannot be controlled.

9. The author states that "The imperceptible effects of music were profound" (line 88). Explain the author's reasoning and tell whether or not it is sound. Support your answer with details from the passage.

_____

_____

_____

_____

_____

_____

_____

_____

_____

_____

10 (a) Why does the author use the phrase "its place in the background of modern medicine" (line 113) to explain the future of music in medicine?

A   Music will always have an impact on medicine in the future.

B   The effects of music as a form of medicine will not be popular.

C   Everyone will not believe the importance of music as a form of medicine.

D   It is important that everyone remembers the role music plays in medicine.

(b) According to the author, in what ways can people change the outcome as stated in Part A? Support your answer with details from the passage.

_____

_____

_____

_____

_____

_____

_____

_____

_____

_____

_____

_____

Glossary

astounded: to feel surprise or shock
She was astounded by the amount of food the young child consumed during the meal.

confounded: to show that one feels annoyed
"Oh that confounded child has once again broken the school rules," remarked the teacher.

implicit: to suggest something without being direct
There was an implicit annoyance in her words when I arrived late for the meeting even though she continued to smile at me.

cringe: to move away out of fear
Bob cringed in fear when the nurse approached with a syringe.

uncharted: referring to something that has not been done before
The boat was moving into uncharted territories and the boatmen were worried that they would be in danger.

Sadlier School

EXERCISE 9

/14
points

Read the passage carefully.

The Student

I was, at that time, a professor at the university teaching psychology to graduate students who were working adults. Limited in the range of their ages but seemingly with wide experience, I was presented with an easy class to teach that summer. In that respect, I was expecting to have witty banter from a dedicated group of speakers
5   eloquent clearly in their respective fields.

Two days after the commencement of the classes, he walked in with an air reeking of belligerence so that I felt the need to halt the class until he settled down. All eyes, including mine, were on him. I must add that it was one of the students who reached for the notes on my table and handed it over to him; such was the
10   anxiety that gripped me like a vise. I was unaccustomed to and disliked students who showed not just apathy but disrespect for their teachers. The university as such was a place where a student like this was an anomaly, making it the perfect place, I felt, for professors like me with just several more years before their retirement.

His name, I found out through a process of elimination on the class list, was
15   Jordan. Younger than the others, he had not stated his place of work. "Where are you working?" I asked him during that first lesson. It took him three seconds to glance up at me. I counted. He shrugged and mumbled; something I could not figure out until one of the students repeated it albeit in a manner that befitted the purpose of his own question.

20   "Oh, I thought the university only takes in graduate students who are working."

I did not answer that, deciding instead to begin the lesson. A general idea of what organizational psychology was about would precede all other more specific topics and I was pleased to see students taking notes and others interrupting my lecture with questions of their own. I welcomed them, using them to explain how
25   they agreed with my knowledge of organizational psychology and correcting some of them. The lesson, the start of what I hoped would be a fulfilling year for the students turned out better than I had expected until it was nearing its closure

when I encouraged the students to clarify any doubts they had. "Perhaps a more interesting lesson would suffice," came that same voice from the back but clearer now, enunciated in a way that emanated sarcasm and an undefined animosity. Undeterred was not what I was feeling but under the circumstances, it was the best emotion to exhibit. A jab at Jordan would heighten the sudden tension in the class and I noticed several hands flying to stack books and papers together in their haste to leave. At that moment, I knew I had to do the same. I was not going to cause a scene and so packed my things with an undisguised efficiency that was meant to hide the unease that was building up within me.

In the second lesson, my intention was to use the information the class shared about their jobs and link it to the theories in organizational psychology. I took it upon myself to assert that the theories were never wrong and when real life examples contradicted the theories, I was quick to tell the students that a change in mindset was necessary. I wanted them to leave the class with well defined ideas of what should or should not be done in the workplace. Had I stopped to think even for a minute, I would have remembered from all my years at the university of letting the fluidity of knowledge be the base at which all lessons were held. Impaired of better judgment by the need to dispense as much knowledge as I could, I watched the students scribbling page after page of notes. There was a silence in the class countered only occasionally by one student or other requesting that I slow down; and this I did until the harsh sound of a deep yawn shot through the air. I stopped mid sentence and glared at Jordan who was at the furthest end of the classroom this time.

"Well…"

"The way you're going on, why would we need to come for class? You're nothing but a walking textbook."

Some of the students I noticed were suppressing the urge to laugh. I too would have laughed if it were someone else in my place now. Those simple words were a blatant reminder of the type of professor that the students needed at this age. I was ashamed that experience had done nothing to aid the inadequacy of how I was feeling. Would my reputation as a professor be tarnished? It was exasperating to know that I had been defeated by a young man who was probably jobless – two traits that I disliked.

In the third lesson, with my lesson learned, I resolved to take the students' experiences more seriously, using them to make genuine links to the theories and accepting that there were areas which the theories failed to explain. I could see that my lesson was better received. Pens still flew over the papers but there were occasional banters and queries were interspersed with information on the theories. At the point when I was the most pleased with myself just as I had been previously, my enthusiasm was jarred. "Some of us would like to go on to the next topic." Once again, the advice was grudgingly taken although in retrospect, a display of my wit would have livened up the lesson and put Jordan in his place.

I chose instead to treat every lesson like a learning point for me as much as it was for the class. But as it was then, none of the results pleased me. My dislike and distrust for Jordan grew by the day. He was certainly a poor student who was not going to do well from the way he behaved. It was a mixture of pride and my passion in the subject that made me summon Jordan to my office before the next lesson. The hands knocked weakly on the door, the legs shuffled slowly into the room and the eyes were downcast. What a failure. My prepared speech somehow did not seem appropriate at that moment so I resorted to asking generic questions that I would have done had I been asked to conduct any interview. But Jordan must have known why he had been called into my office. When there was a silence in our conversation, he broke in with "I'm listening to what you say in class even though I look like I might not be. I tell you things during the class to remind you that you've more under your belt than you can ever imagine and we have just so much that we want to learn from you."

Would the phrase "jaw dropped" even begin to describe the way Jordan had once again managed to stun me? "Don't judge a book by its cover." One of the first idioms I had learned in school came to mind and I realized how true it was. I had been guilty of assuming that Jordan would be a poor student.

It was on 15 August, three months after the start of the course, when I took a stack of written assignments to my office. Jordan's work was placed right at the top – a deliberate action to remind myself that the success of the course was not just about my experience. And I quote, as I flipped to the back of the file to read the journal submitted with the assignment, "It was hardly the agonizing time I thought I would have had being forced back to school before taking over dad's company. The professor changed everything for me, for the better I know but still refuse to admit. I really didn't know as much as I thought I had. What a surprise it has been from a course taught by an elderly man who was probably close to retirement – two traits that I dislike."

I kicked off my shoes, leaned back in my chair and smiled – the contented smile of having met someone who was clearly just like me.

Choose the correct answer and circle the correct letter.

① Why did the author feel that he had "an easy class to teach that summer" (line 3)?
- A His students were working adults.
- B His students had studied at the university previously.
- C His students would have a lot to contribute to the class.
- D His students had expressed interest in being taught by him.

② What is the most important idea conveyed in paragraph 2?
- A Some of the students are more alert than the professor.
- B The arrival of the new student creates tension in the story.
- C The university frowns on students who turn up late for class.
- D The professor is inexperienced when dealing with new students.

③ Why does the author include phrases such as "I felt" (line 13) and "I found out through a process of elimination on the class list" (lines 14) while describing an event in the story?
- A To add humor to the story
- B To emphasize the problems that the professor was facing
- C To incorporate the reasons for the occurrence of the events
- D To show that the professor was someone who disliked encountering problems

④ Why did the other student repeat what Jordan had said?
- A He could not believe what Jordan had said.
- B He took the opportunity to mock Jordan's unemployed status.
- C He knew that the professor could not make out what Jordan had said.
- D He wanted to find out why an unemployed person could take the course.

⑤ (a) Which of the following best supports the idea that the professor was keen to avoid conflict?
- A "The lesson, the start of what I hoped would be a fulfilling year for the students turned out better than I had expected" (lines 26-27)
- B "Undeterred was not what I was feeling but under the circumstances, it was the best emotion to exhibit" (lines 31-32)
- C "I noticed several hands flying to stack books and papers together in their haste to leave" (lines 33-34)
- D "I was pleased to see students taking notes and others interrupting my lecture with questions of their own" (lines 23-24)

(b) What did the professor feel was the best way to avoid conflict? Use the answer in Part A and other details from the paragraph to support your answer.

_____

_____

_____

_____

_____

_____

_____

_____

_____

_____

6 (a) What effect does paragraph 6 have on the reader's understanding of the teacher-student relationship in the class?

A   Only the teacher could impart knowledge to the students.

B   The teacher did not like students who yawned loudly in class.

C   It was better for the students to listen and not speak during the class.

D   Students could only speak if they knew the correct answers to questions asked.

(b) Support your answer in Part A with details from the paragraph.

_____

_____

_____

_____

_____

_____

_____

_____

_____

_____

Sadlier School

7 "I was ashamed that experience had done nothing to aid the inadequacy of how I was feeling." (lines 56-58)

Why did the author feel this way?

A   He was unable to handle difficult students despite having taught for many years.

B   He had taught for many years but he only had knowledge from the textbook.

C   His knowledge was inadequate in reaching out to students who worked in different jobs.

D   His years of teaching should have made him more flexible when imparting knowledge to the students.

8   The author stated that he treated each lesson "like a learning point." (line 70) Explain how he did this and when he did not do this. Support your answer with details from the passage.

_____

_____

_____

_____

_____

_____

_____

_____

_____

_____

_____

_____

9   What effect does the author create by repeating the phrase "two traits that I dislike"? (lines 59-60)

A   Create further tension between Jordan and the professor

B   Show that Jordan is as humorous as the professor

C   Emphasize the similarities between the professor and Jordan

D   Explain the conflict between Jordan and the professor

10 "Don't judge a book by its cover." (line 85) Why is this an appropriate saying to describe the author's behavior? Support your answer with details from the passage.

_____

_____

_____

_____

_____

_____

_____

_____

_____

_____

_____

_____

_____

_____

_____

_____

_____

_____

_____

_____

_____

_____

Glossary

banter: friendly conversation that includes jokes
There was an easy banter between her and her colleagues over lunch.

belligerence: referring to an unfriendly and aggressive manner
His belligerence annoyed his teacher and she decided to call his parents.

anomaly: something that is different from the usual
The doctor found an anomaly when my grandmother went for her health checkup and he asked her to return to the clinic next week.

befitted: suitable for
This sumptuous buffet is befit for someone of royalty.

suffice: enough
Just a salad will suffice for lunch.

animosity: strong dislike
There was so much animosity between the two supervisors in the company that a fierce argument broke out over who would take charge of the project.

blatant: something negative that is easily observed
She had a blatant disregard for school rules.

tarnished: to affect something such as a person's reputation by making it worse
His reputation as an author was tarnished after it was discovered that he had been copying the works of other authors.

exasperating: very annoying
It was exasperating talking to someone who did not speak the same language as me.

jarred: to annoy and shock
His excitement at going on the roller coaster was jarred when there was an announcement that the roller coaster had malfunctioned and would be closed for maintenance.

grudgingly: unwillingly
He apologized grudgingly to his sister as he did not think that it was his fault that her book was torn.

retrospect: to think back and review what happened in the past
In retrospect, I think employees in a company should not be ranked against one another.

INTERMEDIATE

EXERCISE *10*

Read the passage carefully.

The City

"I'll tell you how the city has changed," the lady in the ocher colored dress said
to me. "I went to the cobbler that day, one of those with their tools in a wooden
box that they carry with them. I showed him my slingbacks and he shook his
head. Told me to look for another cobbler! Can you imagine that? Cobblers who
5   used to be calling out for business rejected mine! What has become of this city?"I
nodded at the lady, someone whom I had met at the hotel while having breakfast
one morning. She had seemed like a local so I approached her to ask about unique
sights that only a local would know. She was a new old local. She had returned
after a decade to witness her son's graduation. In just a quarter of an hour, I had
10   found out everything there was to know about her. Why she had returned to the
city, how long she would stay, why she was staying at a hotel and not with her son
and finally, which of the sights would probably appeal to me.

"I promise you the snake charmers will charm you off your feet!" she said a
dozen times since I met her that morning. She had kindly offered to show me around
15   the city when I spoke to her yesterday and I was glad for a traveling companion
but as the morning progressed, I regretted agreeing to the meeting. She was not
any companion I'm sure anyone would have wanted on her travels. I asked about
the bus. These were either single decked ramshackle buses or modern fleets with
double stories, some with an open top. The lady was adamant that I should walk
20   the streets to better enjoy the city sights. About five minutes into the walk, I gazed
longingly at the air conditioned buses that zoomed past me. The air, thick with
pollution, was threatening to make the pills for asthma that I had taken worthless.

I heard the noise long before I saw the birds. Their arrival startled me but the
lady paid no attention to them, ignoring them and even flicking them away when
25   they came too close and circled about her. I, on the other hand, had never had
any bird come so close to me other than my pet parrot that was tame and much

less threatening than the obsidian colored talkative birds. Ignoring them was like ignoring the opened gate of a lion enclosure. I wanted to escape to the awning of a shop but my guide had gone ahead, walking much faster than before. Suddenly, she stopped and I almost knocked right into her. "Shh…There! Just ahead!" I followed her finger but all I saw was a crowded café. The tables lined the pavement, and chairs with their backs against one another making it impossible for any pedestrian to pass. Waiters somehow managed to squeeze their way through, serving cups of hot coffee and plates of cakes or bread.

I peered as hard as I could into the distance. I wanted to move forward but my guide stopped me. I saw no one of value. "Oh come on!" she said impatiently as she tugged at my shirt. I suspected she was not too keen to move forward but was getting equally impatient with my inability to see what she obviously was seeing so clearly. "Over there!" she hissed and my eye drew an imaginary line from her finger to the entrance of the café. A man who looked old with his white colored beard stood just inside the café talking to a younger man, whom from his t-shirt which said "Duff here. How can I help you today?" made it clear that he was the owner of Duff Café. The older man wore an elaborate costume much like what I would expect to see in Arabia. A dark blue costume with gold trimmings reminded me of a cross between a genie and a jester. As he talked, he became more agitated, pointing to somewhere inside the shop. Finally, the owner nodded with a shrug and walked off to speak to more customers who were going in. The older man walked towards the back of the café. He emerged seconds later.

"A snake!" I exclaimed, regretting it immediately.

My guide glanced at me with an amused look on her face. "Indeed, it is," she said. "You wanted to see something unique didn't you? Well here it is a snake charmer at work."

"I don't understand. Where are the…"

"Round woven baskets and eerie pipe music?" she interjected.

I wanted to nod but before I could do that, she patted my arm and said, "See, I told you the city has changed. You won't see those around here anymore. They want to make more money from their trade, so they have to find ways to do so. You see, they are like everyone else. The charm of this place is fast eroding and will soon be overtaken by nothing but greed. There is nothing attractive about this place."

60   I only heard bits and pieces of what she was saying for I was now focused on the scene unfolding before my eyes. On a table outside the café where two customers were already seated, the snake charmer placed his newly caught snake at the edge. Then, taking a small pipe out of his pocket, he began playing a haunting tune that the snake immediately responded to. It twisted its body first to the left

65   and then the right, much like a dancer would. Its body glistened in the morning sun, sparkling like its skin was covered with diamonds. Then, it slowly uncoiled itself, rising upwards like the flame from a fire. The customers backed away as the snake straightened pointing arrow-like at one of the customers. Some of them applauded but most of them were shocked by what was happening. "Hey! Get

70   rid of it! This is not a circus. This is a reputable café. No snakes should be allowed here!" came a shout from one of the tables. "No, let him continue. I've never seen a snake charmer before. Can snakes really hear music?" another shout emanated from a corner. "Where did the snake come from? He wasn't holding one earlier. I noticed him. Was the snake already in the café?"

75   Duff, the owner, seemed to realize that trouble was brewing and he hurried up to the snake charmer, pressing a bundle of notes into his hand and whispering into his ear. The snake charmer smiled and nodded. Shoving the notes into his pocket, he grabbed the snake and left, walking in the direction of another row of shops. "Everything's all right now. There are no more snakes. No snakes in the

80   café, everyone. It's safe."

I realized what the snake charmer had done. It was probably much more than what he would get if he had just set up his basket by the side of the road.

"Saw that? Now, let me show you the activities along the river. We won't be able to get too near though at this time," she said as she glanced at her watch. "It

85   can get quite crowded in the morning but we will try," she continued with a grin as she hastened southwest.

I was beginning to think that my companion was wrong about the city. Perhaps it was not as simple as when she first knew it, but it certainly hadn't lost its charm and whatever vestiges of tradition that remained drew me even more to the place.

Choose the correct answer and circle the correct letter.

1 How does the question "Can you imagine that?" (line 4) add to the reader's understanding of the lady?

    A   The lady was appalled by how the city had changed.

    B   The lady disliked cobblers who were rude.

    C   The lady felt that the city was a terrible place to live in.

    D   The lady no longer liked living in the city.

2 What does "new old local" (line 8) tell the reader about the lady?

    A   She did not recognize the city that she had grown up in.

    B   She no longer felt comfortable in the city.

    C   She wished the city was the same as it had been in the past.

    D   She no longer wanted to live in the city.

3 The lady said "I promise you the snake charmers will charm you off your feet" (line 13) to show that _____.

    A   she liked snake charmers

    B   she wanted to watch the snake charmers

    C   she knew the appeal that snake charmers had

    D   she had a personal connection with the snake charmers

4 Which of the following is the most important detail that can be determined from paragraph 2 about the author's relationship with the lady?

    A   The author disliked the lady tremendously.

    B   The author did not know the lady very well.

    C   The lady wanted only the best for the author.

    D   The lady paid no heed to the author's feelings.

5 The author said that "ignoring them was like ignoring the opened gate of a lion enclosure" (lines 27-28). The author used this simile to emphasize that the birds _____.

    A   had to be taken care of in a zoo

    B   should have been kept in cages

    C   would harm the people on the streets

    D   were hungry and would eat anything

6. What does the direct speech and dialogue from the time the café is observed until the snake charmer is spotted by the author reveal about the lady's character?

   A   Friendly and enthusiastic

   B   Confused and domineering

   C   Persistent and overly excitable

   D   Confident and slightly overbearing

7. (a) Which of the following best explains why the lady wanted the author to see the snake charmer at the café?

   A   To find out what snake charmers did

   B   To identify snake charmers' costumes

   C   To prove that snake charmers still existed

   D   To learn that snake charmers could be found in cafes

   (b) Based on your answer in Part A, what difficulties did the author face? Support your answer with details from the passage.

   _____

   _____

   _____

   _____

   _____

   _____

   _____

   _____

   _____

   _____

8. (a) "I realized what the snake charmer had done. It was probably much more than what he would get if he had just set up his basket by the side of the road." (lines 81-82)

   Why are the author's thoughts incorporated into the story at this point?

   A   To portray the charm of the city

   B   To emphasize the author's thoughts at that moment

   C   To suggest that the snake charmer was in dire straits

   D   To show that the author was amused by what she had seen

(b) Provide another reason other than the one given in Part A that gives the reader a better understanding of the story.

_____

_____

_____

_____

_____

_____

_____

_____

_____

_____

⑨ In the passage, how does the author's description of the snake convey both a positive and negative attitude about the snake? Use details from the passage to support your answer. In your response,
- identify examples that support both a positive and a negative attitude
- explain how these examples support your answer

_____

_____

_____

_____

_____

_____

_____

_____

_____

_____

_____

10 The author and the lady had different opinions of the "charm" of the city. How does this difference affect the reader's impression of the city? Support your answer using details from the passage.

_____

_____

_____

_____

_____

_____

_____

_____

_____

_____

_____

_____

_____

_____

_____

Glossary

ocher: referring to a reddish yellow color
The bouquet of flowers was a mix of pink, blue and ocher.

ramshackle: referring to a building or a vehicle that is in poor condition
He has been driving the ramshackle car for years but he refuses to replace it because it has sentimental value for him.

obsidian: referring to a type of black glass
Did the people in the past use deposits of obsidian to make tools?

reputable: referring to something that people have a good opinion of
When doing research for your project, you should look for information from reputable sources so that the information you obtain will be accurate.

vestiges: small amounts of something
All vestiges of power were removed from the royal family once the system of government was changed.

DATE: .... NAME: ....

CLASS: ....

/16
points

EXERCISE 11

Read the passage carefully.

Tchoukball

Sporting activities have long been embraced as a way to increase one's level of fitness and, in the case of team sports, promote camaraderie among friends. However, intimately associated with many familiar sports is also the heightened risk of injury during play. Injuries can range from a minor twisted ankle to a life-
5   threatening impact injury. The rates of injury unsurprisingly increase with sports that require a high level of physical contact between its players, as seen in games such as rugby or football. It was his dogged determination to reduce the risk of serious injury associated with sports that led Dr. Hermann Brandt, an eminent Swiss Biologist, to invent Tchoukball in 1970. He carried out a critical analysis of
10   team sports and published a paper entitled "A Scientific Criticism of Team Games," which won him the acclaimed Thulin Prize and led to the development of the ideal team sport Dr. Brandt believed would be universally accepted in time to come. Unfortunately, Dr. Brandt passed away in 1972 before he could see the fruit of his research and efforts. However, his contribution to the sporting world has made a
15   lasting impact in more ways than one.

Pronounced "Chuke-ball" and named for the sound a rebounding ball makes off a Tchoukball frame, this game consists of features that are both unique and common. It incorporates elements found in volleyball, basketball and handball. Tchoukball has steadily risen in popularity from its humble beginnings as a theoretical concept
20   and is now played in many countries worldwide including France, Germany, Italy, Brazil, the United States of America, Taiwan, Hong Kong and Singapore. A likely reason for the popularity it enjoys is the all-inclusive nature of the game. With the motto "A Sport For All," Tchoukball welcomes players of all shapes and sizes. Tchoukball holds high standards of safety by reducing injury. Physical contact
25   between players is kept to a minimum. Players are not allowed to intercept a pass or tackle another player during the course of the game. Another feature of Tchoukball is its emphasis on maintaining a high standard of ethics. Underhanded play is not condoned and the Tchoukball Charter even has regulations that restrict advertising and sponsorship from alcohol and tobacco companies.

30   Tchoukball consists of seven players on each team and is played with a ball on a rectangular court not unlike a netball or volleyball court. On both ends of the court, two framed square nets measuring 90 centimeters on each side form the "goal" or "rebound frames." A large semi-circle runs around the bottom of the frame, forming a "D" shape. This is known as the forbidden zone. Players are not

35   allowed to enter this zone during gameplay. The objective of the game is to score as many goals as possible for one's team within an allotted time. Players throw the ball from one to another to make attacks on the rebound frame. Players fall into three categories, namely Wingers, Forward Pivots and Center Pivots. Goals are scored when the ball hits the rebound frame and bounces off so that it lands over

40   the semi-circle boundary of the "D" or forbidden zone. Players of a team pass the ball among themselves. Once a goal is scored, possession of the ball is given to the opposing team. Possession of the ball also goes to the opposing team when a player commits a foul. While opposing players are not allowed to intercept passes, they are allowed to protect the ball when a shot is taken at the rebound frame.

45   Unlike many other games, players can score for their team on both ends of the court. In addition, points are awarded to the opposing team in a number of situations, making accuracy a key component of play. Teams lose points to their opponents when they try to score and miss the rebound frame completely, when the ball rebounds and lands out of the playing area or within the forbidden zone,

50   or when the ball bounces off the rebound frame and touches the player who threw the ball.

        Other key rules of the game are easily encompassed in the Rule of Three: a player can hold the ball for a maximum of three seconds and take up to three steps while holding the ball; three passes are allowed between team mates before a shot

55   at the goal must be taken, and teams can score a maximum of three goals at the same rebound frame before the next shot must be scored at the rebound frame on the opposite end of the court. These simplify the game and make it more appealing to many.

        In play, Tchoukball translates into a fast-paced and spectacular game where

60   an international standard player making a shot at the rebound frame can jump up to 5 feet in height and throw the ball at speeds of up to 62 miles per hour. Yet, even at this level, injuries in the game are few. At an amateur stage, players of all levels of fitness can hone their skills and confidence through recreational practice of this game. On a professional level, the rules of the game are enough to protect the players

65   from suffering any unnecessary injuries. Of course, injuries have occurred but in comparison to other sports, Tchoukball has a lower rate of injuries.

Apart from having been deliberately fashioned to reduce injury while enabling one to fully enjoy physical activities, Tchoukball is also known for the way it promotes cohesion, goodwill and collaboration among its players. With possession of the ball passing on to the players from the opposing team once a goal is scored, the need to tackle and inadvertently injuring players from the opposing team is drastically reduced.

Dr. Brandt believed that the perfect sport would take human nature into consideration and allow for the realization of an individual's potential in a holistic manner while promoting collaboration and growth in social relationships. Respect for self and others is a value held in high esteem by Dr. Brandt and players are cautioned not to lose sight of this in their struggle for prestige and honor. Stronger players are encouraged to look out for weaker players and guide them in the game, all the while collectively striving for a feeling of oneness in a common effort to play the game well.

Tchoukball is steadily making its presence felt in Physical Education classes in the United States of America. Shari Frank, a middle school teacher in Northern Virginia encountered the relatively unknown game at a conference for Physical Education teachers and subsequently introduced it to her students. Apart from introducing it to her school, she went on to represent the U.S. at an international level and has also worked to spread awareness of the sport through presenting at conferences. In her experience playing the game in a classroom setting, she found it to be a team sport that, unlike other sports, is easy to grasp and enjoy playing with anyone. In a co-ed middle school setting, it was a game that could be played with both boys and girls without concerns about proximity issues. She was also able to include students with disabilities in the game and also found that its cooperative nature made it hard for one player to dominate the game. At the same time, Tchoukball's unique nature posed a challenge in changing the mindsets of her students. While many competitive team sports require a focus on guarding an opponent or intercepting a pass, Tchoukball players need to learn to override their natural response to do so.

In his aspiration to make sporting activities more enjoyable and beneficial for all, Dr. Hermann Brandt created a distinct sport that, while still considered a minority game, is certainly making ripples across the globe. Tchoukball enthusiasts hope that it will one day be recognized as an Olympic sport. Apart from its focus on building one's form, it has made its mark in the way that it embraces values that promote cooperation and cohesion among people. In the words of the man himself, "The aim of physical activities is not to create champions, but to contribute to the building of a more harmonious society." In a world where competitiveness and prestige are often valued above other things, we stand to learn a great deal from an obscure sport that celebrates just the opposite.

Choose the correct answer and circle the correct letter.

1. How does the author use the first paragraph to enhance the reader's interest in reading the rest of the passage?

   A   Emphasize the importance of playing sports

   B   Highlight the popularity of team sports

   C   Explain the problems associated with team sports

   D   Identify the reason for the absence of safe sports

2. What does "dogged determination" (line 7) tell the reader about team sports?

   A   It is difficult to be injury free when playing sports.

   B   People are unwilling to play new sports.

   C   Team sports are unpopular because they cause injuries.

   D   Some dangerous team sports should be banned.

3. The second paragraph identifies "features of Tchoukball that are both unique and common." Explain what the author means using details from the passage to support your answer.

   _____

   _____

   _____

   _____

   _____

   _____

   _____

   _____

   _____

   _____

   _____

   _____

   _____

   _____

4 What is the main way paragraph 3 enhances the reader's understanding of the passage?

A   A description of how easy it is to play the game

B   A clear and detailed explanation of how the game is played

C   Explanation of how safety is incorporated into the game

D   Comparison between the game and other well known games

5 "These simplify the game and make it more appealing to many." (lines 57-58)
What does the sentence above tell the reader about those who enjoy playing Tchoukball? Support your answer with details from the passage.

_____

_____

_____

_____

_____

_____

_____

_____

_____

_____

6 Explain how Tchoukball encompasses aspects of both an individualistic and collective nature? Support your answer with details from the passage.

_____

_____

_____

_____

_____

_____

_____

_____

_____

7 Who is probably the target audience for this passage?
A   Those who have started playing Tchoukball
B   Those who enjoy individual sports
C   Physical education teachers looking to introduce new sports
D   Sportsmen who are striving for prestige and honor in sports

8 What does the phrase "made its mark" (line 101) tell the reader about how new sports can become part of the popular sport culture?
A   Team sports are becoming more popular today than in the past.
B   Everyone who plays new team sports does so to make new friends.
C   Prestige cannot be obtained if teammates are expected to cooperate.
D   To gain acceptance, new sports must address current concerns in sports.

9 How does the phrase "ripples across the globe" (line 99) explain the author's opinion of the future of Tchoukball? Support your answer with details from the passage.

_____

_____

_____

_____

_____

_____

_____

_____

_____

_____

_____

_____

_____

_____

_____

_____

10. The author states that one can "learn a great deal from an obscure sport." (lines 105-106) Explain how this phrase both contradicts and supports the information presented in the passage. Support your answer with details from the passage.

_____

_____

_____

_____

_____

_____

_____

_____

_____

_____

_____

_____

Glossary

embraced: to accept something new such as new ideas or new opinions
In recent years, the school has embraced a new method of student assessment which veers away from the focus on pen and paper examinations.

camaraderie: feeling of friendship with others when working together in a group
The feeling of camaraderie developed among the group of workers who came together to work on the year-long project.

dogged: to be very determined
Her dogged determination to succeed as an athlete was what helped her to overcome all the obstacles that came her way.

condoned: to accept a particular behavior
She condoned the eating of cakes and cookies, preferring her children to eat only healthy food.

encompass: to include
Changes to the national health policy encompass everyone from the young to the old.

honed: to improve on a skill
To hone her basketball skills, she practiced for two hours every day after school.

ADVANCED

EXERCISE 12

/16
points

Read the passage carefully.

First Day at Work

I was a month shy of my seventeenth birthday when I went to work for Mr. Dale in his fruit store. Nothing could be simpler than packing a couple of fruit into boxes. Even carrying crates of heavy fruit was not daunting for someone of my stature. And so, I eagerly arrived at the fruit store the following Monday morning,
5 certain that I would prove to my father and Mr. Dale that it was not connections that would make me the most sought after worker in the store.

Mr. Dale's store was the largest fruit store in the neighborhood and one of the most popular. My father and Mr. Dale grew up in the same neighborhood way back when everyone was either a farmer or a factory worker. Their parents had worked
10 at the same factory and so my father and Mr. Dale found themselves spending time together at school and later in the evenings as well when their parents would meet for dinners. Even when my father started work and traveled to New Hampshire to work as an attorney in one of the most promising law firms there and Mr. Dale, came of age and developed an interest in starting a business, they both continued to
15 keep in touch. They would spend the occasional weekend fishing at the lake where they used to play. Mr. Dale closed his fruit store and traveled to New Hampshire to attend a ceremony celebrating my father's inclusion as one of the partners in the law firm. When I was born, Mr. Dale arrived with a large fruit basket, twice my size then, and spent a couple of days at my house. It was not surprising then when
20 my father decided to open his own law firm, he decided to move back to where his dearest friend lived. "There is no better place than home where Fred is." I had overheard him telling my mother one day. Fred, of course, was Mr. Dale.

So it was that Monday morning, when I arrived and saw a truck outside the store. I rolled up my sleeves and quickened my steps. "Let me," I said in a voice
25 that I hoped sounded gruff enough as I reached for the huge crate of apples that Mr. Dale had just unloaded from the truck. I received a cold hard stare from the boss that I was to be working for the whole summer and whom I was counting on to provide me with the money I needed to buy my new skateboard. His fingers tightened around the crate and he brushed past me as he carried it effortlessly back

30　into his store. I noticed a couple more crates in the truck but I held back. Mr. Dale appeared barely a minute later and this time he carried two crates back into the store. I saw dark green avocados in one and potatoes in another. Suddenly, I felt myself shrinking. Mr. Dale was no taller than five feet and so scrawny, one would think he was malnourished.

35　　　I waited outside the shop that first day until the truck had left and I was certain that Mr. Dale was ready for me. I stepped into the shop and paused at the entrance. I was overwhelmed by the smell as much as I was by the darkness. "Come on, boy. Stop standing there. Get started. You'll be paid a day's work you know." I followed the sound of his voice and found myself at the back of the store where I had to shield
40　my eyes from the light that shone from a single bare bulb dangling on the ceiling. "The good ones here and the bad ones over there," he gestured and left the room. I stared after him. The sense of uncertainty was tremendous. I did not dare to ask any questions both from what had just happened that morning and from my own pride. My father must have boasted about me. I gritted my teeth and squatted in
45　front of a crate that was overflowing with apples. I could do it.

　　　About twenty minutes later, the crate was still filled with apples. The "good" basket only contained a handful of apples while the "bad" basket contained twice the number of apples. My insides were doing flip flops when Mr. Dale walked back into the shop, dragging his feet in a way that created a sound I hated but which I
50　later learned to appreciate. "Haven't you ever been to the market with your mother, boy? Don't you know what a good apple is from a bad one?" I squatted helplessly next to Mr. Dale as he tossed first one apple and then the next into either basket. "Look, son. You put one of these in the "good" basket. See the dent at the bottom? Dents are never good in anything, are they? That's not going to go down well with
55　my customers you know. They come from all over and most of them know their fruit." After a while, he moved to the side and gestured at the remaining apples in the crate. "Go on." I picked up the apples nervously. I wondered if he could tell that my hands were shaking. I had never felt so embarrassed in my life. Mr. Dale had made it look so simple, like knowledge that was so basic it seemed like I came
60　from another planet. I hated apples after that. I would not want to eat another apple ever again even though it had always been my favorite fruit.

　　　My next task was to sweep the floor of the store which I realized later that I had to do almost every hour for vegetable leaves and fruit stems would be littered everywhere. Initially, it was just leaves and bits of dirt that dropped from the crates
65　but once the store was opened, the more customers there were, the dirtier the floor became. Some children grabbed tomatoes and dropped them on the floor, only for them to be crushed when they played catch in the confined space. I hated having

to wipe up the bright red splatter with the tiny cloth that Mr. Dale gave me and having to rinse it and clean that same spot numerous times before all traces of the smashed tomato were gone. Mr. Dale wanted the store pristine as ridiculous as that was. I felt that the job was beneath me and I wanted to do more. Why couldn't I be the one seated behind the counter? I could help pack the fruit and vegetables. I would be good at that. But Mr. Dale had other ideas. He dominated the counter, doing everything from scanning to packing and collecting the money. Perhaps he didn't trust me with the money, I reasoned. After the earlier experience, I did not dare say anything except to do whatever I was told.

At about 4 o'clock that day, a group of ladies entered the shop. I wanted to retreat to the small room at the back, having just swept the floor. But Mr. Dale had other ideas. "Come here, boy. Come and help Mrs. Sprits with her basket." And I found myself taking on yet another task – carrying the baskets for well groomed ladies as they searched for what they wanted and tossed them into the basket. It was demeaning. This was not the job that I had envisioned. Even if Mr. Dale wanted to work me like a horse, he did not have to treat me like a slave. I was determined not to spend the rest of my summer in this way. Yet, the money was a draw. I would be able to pay for the skateboard that I so wanted and had been staring at for the past three months. I might even have some money left over for the cap that I wanted. Mr. Dale was paying me well, I had to admit although from the look on his face at times, I wondered if he had been compelled to pay me more than he wanted to because of my father.

Choose the correct answer and circle the correct letter.

1. What does "Nothing could be simpler than packing a couple of fruit into boxes" (lines 2-3) tell you about how the author felt about the job?
   A   He felt that the job was beneath him.
   B   He felt that the job was too simple for him.
   C   He felt that the job would not be challenging.
   D   He felt that the job would be similar to other jobs.

2. How were the author's chances of getting the job affected by his father's relationship with Mr. Dale?
   A   The author's father and Mr. Dale were close friends.
   B   Mr. Dale had promised to let the author work in his shop.
   C   Mr. Dale did everything the author's father told him to.
   D   The author's father wanted to maintain close relations with Mr. Dale.

3 What does "Their parents had worked at the same factory and so my father and Mr. Dale found themselves spending time together at school and later in the evenings as well when their parents would meet for dinners." (lines 9-12) tell you about the neighborhood in which the author's father grew up in?

A The people in the neighborhood kept to themselves.

B The neighborhood consisted of a closed knit community.

C There were not many places to work at in the neighborhood.

D It was a small neighborhood where the people led simple lives.

4 (a) "There is no better place than home where Fred is." (line 21)
What effect does the author create by including his father's exact words in a description of the past?

A It adds humor to the story.

B It shows that the author had a good memory.

C It causes the reader to pay more attention to the author's father.

D It emphasizes the friendship between the author's father and Mr. Dale.

(b) Based on the quoted sentence in Part A, explain the relationship between "home" and "Fred". Use details from the passage to support your answer.

_____

_____

_____

_____

_____

_____

_____

_____

_____

_____

_____

_____

_____

_____

5 (a) What impact does the description of Mr. Dale when the author first arrived at the store have on the development of the story?

    A   Adds confusion in the story

    B   Creates tension in the story

    C   Causes a comedic effect in the story

    D   Highlights the main problem in the story

(b) Using details from the passage, explain your answer in Part A.

_____

_____

_____

_____

_____

_____

_____

_____

_____

_____

6 The author said that he felt himself "shrinking." (line 33) Using details from the passage, explain what he means by this.

_____

_____

_____

_____

_____

_____

_____

_____

_____

_____

7 Which of the following best states the main idea of paragraph four?

A "My father must have boasted about me." (line 44)

B "The sense of uncertainty was tremendous." (line 42)

C "I was overwhelmed by the smell as much as I was by the darkness." (line 37)

D "I did not dare to ask any questions both from what had just happened that morning and from my own pride." (lines 42-44)

8 The author felt like he "came from another planet." (lines 59-60) Why did he feel that way? Support your answer with details from the passage.

_____

_____

_____

_____

_____

_____

_____

_____

_____

_____

_____

_____

_____

_____

_____

_____

_____

9 (a) What problems did the author face when he was given the task of keeping the store clean?

A He did not know how to clean the floor.

B He did not like such backbreaking tasks.

C He felt that the floor was clean enough and did not have to be cleaned.

D He could not keep up with the mess that was being created on the floor.

(b)   Besides the problem mentioned in Part A, what other problems did the author face in paragraph 6?

_____

_____

_____

_____

_____

_____

_____

_____

_____

_____

_____

_____

10   The author states "Even if Mr. Dale wanted to work me like a horse, he did not have to treat me like a slave." (lines 82-83) Explain the different opinion the author had of the job compared to Mr. Dale. Use details from the passage to support your answer.

_____

_____

_____

_____

_____

_____

_____

_____

_____

_____

_____

_____

Glossary

shy: to be less than something
Sue was just shy of getting fifty percent of the votes to become part of the class committee.

stature: referring to someone's height or size
We did not expect someone of her stature to be able to lift such heavy boxes so effortlessly.

gruff: a rough and low voice
My father often spoke to us in a gruff voice but we knew that he cared for us.

overwhelmed: to feel so strongly about an emotion that it affects how we think
She was overwhelmed by excitement when she stepped into Disneyland.

pristine: to be very clean
Although the building was very old, its interior was still pristine due to the hard work of the many cleaners.

envisioned: to imagine what might happen in the future
She envisioned a life in the countryside with her husband after her children had grown up and moved out.

ADVANCED

EXERCISE *13*

/16
points

Read the passage carefully.

Signs and Communication

What is communication? Communication is talking to one another; it is
television; it is texting one another; it is a performance;it is our attire, our hairstyle
- the list is endless. Communication is therefore a complex process of information
exchange by and among people. Since it is a complex process, many communication
5   theories have been coined from different perspectives for explanation and guidance,
such that effective communication can be achieved.

One theoretical perspective called "structuralism" particularly sees
communication as being dependant on the structures of society, where meaning
of the information is decoded according to one's environment and experiences.
10 Semiotics is often referred to as the science of signs and is an area of study that
delves into the meanings conveyed through signs and symbols and states that
they can be "coded" and "decoded" differently in different societal settings and
cultures. As we better understand what signs are, we will discover, the role of signs
in communication in today's multi-faceted society.

15 Signs, which are artefacts or acts that refer to something other than themselves,
relate differently to one another and produce different meanings in different systems.
Signs exist to represent, or to indicate the presence or occurrence of something
else. Each sign has a signifier and a signified side, which are the apparent and the
connotation respectively. The apparent refers to the obvious or literal meaning of
20 the sign while connotations are subtleties interpreted differently due to a difference
in location, tradition, upbringing or culture, or ideology, which is essentially our
learned value system. Words are considered signs as they represent something
other than the letters themselves, and they also produce different meanings in
different systems. Understanding and communicating are often set according to
25 our ideology and hence, signs may look the same but not carry the same meaning
and value to different groups of people.

Signs can be divided into three categories: icons, indexes, and symbols. An icon resembles, to some extent, the object it signifies; an index is causally connected to the object it signifies; a symbol is subjectively and culturally linked to the object it signifies. An example of an icon would be a photograph, which can be said to be an icon of the people photographed or an icon of the activity that was photographed. An example of an index would be screaming, where it can be said to be an index of fear if the person screamed as a result of being scared or an index of excitement if the screaming was a result of winning the first prize in a draw. A country's flag would be an excellent example of a symbol where its meaning cannot be made out from its appearance and must be learned. Despite its categorization, the same sign can serve as an icon, index or symbol, all at the same time. Although signs are not necessarily visual, many signs have important visual aspects such as color, size, space, shape and contrast, which are subjected to different interpretations.

After understanding what signs are, one then wonders what their role in communication is. In all societies, symbols preceded writing and were the basis of the written script. Thus, signs are created by humans as a form of communication to transmit social meanings, which are derived from different ideologies. This is to say that signs enable the sending of messages at a fundamental level and at a more complex level, the exchange of information among humans. Signs can also reflect ideology, aiding the interpretation of different realities. For example, white flowers might signify elegance, bliss and purity for some but symbolize death, mourning and sadness for others. As the world is made up of different cultures and traditions, people often hold different beliefs and values from one another. Hence, such information is our source of knowledge and understanding of the wider society, which will enable more effective communication.

In addition, non-verbal signs may also reinforce verbal communication. These signs may give additional information such as emotions to the receiver or serve to emphasize certain points. However, as these signs are often unconscious, and built according to ideology, they can be constantly encoded and decoded accordingly to produce powerful meanings. For example, a "thank you" accompanied by a bow might add sincerity and formality to the appreciation and be appropriate for certain groups of people such as royalties but inappropriate or excessive to others.

Today, the role of signs and ideology in communication can be extended to the design of one's text when we send messages. It is now possible to use various programs to manipulate and change font faces, positioning, graphics and designs, which can help to turn mere words into visual statements with symbolic meaning. For example, clear font faces, headings, and consistent formatting are commonly used in business documents to symbolize the importance, discipline, and seriousness of the document and person. The person receiving the document will then be able to tell its professionalism, as opposed to a writing littered with fanciful font face and inconsistent paragraphing.

Let's use an example of an article with an accompanying photograph to illustrate the role "signs" play in communication. An article itself usually details the series of events and we usually derive the main bulk of our understanding of the situation or event through these linguistic symbols, decoding them according to our learned systems. However, an accompanying photograph to an article or news report, seemingly adds depth to the information provided. As mentioned earlier, a photograph is considered an icon. It is an icon of the people photographed, the place photographed, or the activity photographed, as it is an apparent representation of the event itself. However, the people and objects in the photograph can also be considered as symbols of something else. For example if it was Tim Cook, CEO of Apple, who was photographed, he can also be considered as a symbol of Apple. Depending on our learned systems and culture, we are also able to decode for further information such as his work environment and his disposition, through his posture, expression, and attire. For example, if he is smiling in the picture and adopts a relaxed stance, it could possibly signify that he possesses an easy-going disposition, since smiling is an index of positive feelings and is a universally welcoming gesture. Through his dress, we will also be able to get an indication of his job nature or work environment. Should he be dressed in casual clothing, it could possibly be decoded as inappropriate and sloppy in some cultures, especially considering his professional status as a CEO. However, since Apple has earned itself a reputation for being an unconventional and creative company, his casual dress directly conveys this type of work culture.

Other aspects of a photograph such as size, colors, and positioning, also potentially give us additional information regarding the accompanying article. If Tim Cook is in the center of the photograph, and the article is about the launch of the latest iPhone model, it could be to emphasize his level of importance behind the Apple brand or the success of the latest launch. On the contrary, if the iPhone takes on centre-stage for the same article, the message would be decoded differently, such that more emphasis might be placed on the features of the product. The color of

Sadlier School

Tim Cook's attire could also give us good indication of his nature, which the article might not touch on. If he is dressed in bright vibrant colors, it could be indicative of a cheerful and dynamic nature, while dull colors such as black, navy, or gray signifies

100 more of a somber and serious disposition. Additionally, distances between people who were photographed and space allocation of certain objects also gives us more in depth understanding of the intended message. For instance, if Tim Cook was photographed with two accompanying colleagues and leans closer to one than the other, this could point towards him having a more amicable relationship with one

105 than the other. Imagine this picture to be take infront of the Apple headquarters: if significant photo space is allocated to the office building, it could be to signify the company's standing in the industry, its success, and stability.

Signs provide a basis for communication and continue to be important even with the advent of technology. The analysis largely depends on one's ideological

110 background and knowledge. What is interpreted by one person is not indicative of what another person, who has a different system of understanding, might interpret. Thus, while we might try to provide a vague framework for an analysis of signs, there is no fixed code that one can use in specific situations and what is interpreted here, today, might not be true elsewhere, tomorrow.

Choose the correct answer and circle the correct letter.

 1 Why does the author list the different types of communication in the first paragraph?
  A   To explain why people should communicate frequently
  B   To highlight the extent at which communication takes place today
  C   To emphasize the importance of communicating in different ways
  D   To encourage the reader to think about how he communicates

 2 Which of the following explains why structuralism is important in the understanding of how people communicate today?
  A   "meaning of the information is decoded according to one's environment and experiences" (lines 8-9)
  B   "Each sign has a signifier and a signified side" (line 18)
  C   "Signs, which are artefacts or acts that refer to something other than themselves" (line 15)
  D   "role of signs in communication in today's multi-faceted society" (lines 13-14)

3 (a) The author differentiates between apparent and connotation. What does this differentiation indicate about communication?

    A   A sign used during communication can mean different things to different people.

    B   People communicate based on how they have been brought up.

    C   It is important to analyze signs that are used in communication.

    D   No sign is unique to a particular group of people.

    (b) Explain the answer in Part A in terms of the different categories of signs. Support your answer with details from the passage.

    _____

    _____

    _____

    _____

    _____

    _____

    _____

    _____

    _____

    _____

    _____

    _____

    _____

4 (a) The author says that signs allow the "sending of messages at a fundamental level and at a more complex level." (lines 44-45) How does this affect the reader's understanding of signs?

    A   There are many different types of signs.

    B   Signs are complicated.

    C   We use many signs each time we communicate.

    D   Signs are crucial features of communication.

(b) Explain the answer in Part A based on the concepts "fundamental level" and "complex level" using details from the passage.

_____

_____

_____

_____

_____

_____

_____

_____

_____

_____

_____

_____

_____

5 How does the author explain the pervasiveness of signs in communication today?

A   Definition of signs with examples

B   Simple to complicated types of signs

C   Different reasons for using signs

D   Ways to understand different signs

6 Which of the following is a conclusion about signs and technology?

A   Signs are no longer necessary with technology.

B   Technology simplifies the way signs can be communicated.

C   Technology has resulted in new types of signs.

D   Signs will make it difficult to use technology.

7 Which of the following is not used by the author to explain the significance of signs today?

A   Easily recognized examples

B   Chronological description of signs

C   How signs gained social significance

D   Theoretical explanation of signs

8 The author uses the phrase "Let's use an example" (line 68) when introducing a new paragraph in the passage. How does this affect the tone of the passage?

_____

_____

_____

_____

_____

_____

_____

_____

_____

_____

_____

_____

9 What additional information is provided in the last paragraph that is not mentioned in the rest of the passage? Explain why this information is important. Support your answer with details from the passage.

_____

_____

_____

_____

_____

_____

_____

_____

_____

_____

_____

_____

10. The author uses a photograph in an article to explain the importance of signs. Explain how the photograph is an adequate description of signs used in communication. Support your answer with details from the passage.

_____

_____

_____

_____

_____

_____

_____

_____

_____

_____

_____

_____

_____

_____

_____

_____

_____

_____

Glossary

excessive: more than necessary
  She poured an excessive amount of oil into the pan so she had to pour some out before she started cooking.

manipulate: to work with the information obtained to achieve what is required
  Please manipulate the graphics to fit the page.

disposition: one's temperament or his character that affects his behavior
  He has such a pleasant disposition that everyone who knows him enjoys his company.

unconventional: different from the usual
  Her unconventional dressing style attracted the attention of many people as she walked along the streets.

vague: not clear
  He only has a vague idea of what he wants and not a firm plan.

ADVANCED

EXERCISE *14*

/16 points

Read the passage carefully.

The Mission

I stood at the furthest corner of the room, gently swirling the glass of dull orange liquid in my hand and occasionally sipping the liquid in my hand, trying to look indifferent yet observant to my surroundings. Occasionally, I took out my cellphone and glanced at it, tossed my hair back and let my eyes wander around the room. I
5   never let my eyes rest on any one thing or person for more than two seconds but I was alert and observant at the same time. That's what the book said. I took out my cellphone to glance at it again. Barely three minutes had passed.

"Hi, haven't seen you at the office before. You came with someone?" a pleasant voice from an equally pleasant face said just in my ear. I jumped, almost spilling my
10   drink. A few drops had splattered on the carpet. Now, I must clarify that on other occasions, I would never have reacted like that. However, when I was on a mission, I hated such rude interruptions to my train of thoughts or a lack of it.

The girl, around my age, with the same sun bleached hair as mine was grinning. She was clearly amused. I blushed, stared down at my drink and counted till two
15   before gazing at her and nodding. "George. I was supposed to meet him here, but apparently he's late." I shrugged, hoping that my feigned disinterest was working and she would leave me alone soon. Where was George anyway? He had told me to come as his companion, would introduce me to the daughter of the company director and while we hit it off talking about the latest designer bags which she was
20   apparently very interested in, he would find a way to grab the access card from her bag so that he could enter the out of bounds computer room in the basement of the office building which was just across the road from where we were. This was almost similar to what I did at the last dinner party where I had spent the better half of an hour chatting about thoroughbred horses to the young son of a billionaire. He
25   was charming and I almost forgot where I was. We hit it off the moment we met each other. I didn't mind such missions. George paid me a handsome amount that helped me to pay my rent for the apartment in the city.

"Ah George," the girl mumbled, raising her eyebrows slightly.

30 Alarm bells rang in my head. I did not like the look on her face. Did she know something I didn't? Did she know something about me or my mission? Suddenly, I had images of myself being pinned down by two burly men in a small dank room. They would tie me with ropes and torture me with all sorts of water torturing devices I had seen in espionage movies. I would refuse to reveal who I was working for and they would torture me further. Eventually, I would tell them a lie, that would sound 35 convincing enough for them to free me and I would escape before my captors found out that I had deceived them. I would be a hero, a heroine actually, and I would be ushered into the private office of the president where we would have a tete-a-tete.

"Well, there he is. I think he just arrived," the girl pointed at the entrance where the spotlight shone right on George just as he stepped through the doorway.

40 "Oh, yes, yes," I muttered, realizing that my work was about to begin. I had no idea why George needed to get into the computer room of all these large companies or how he managed to get himself invited to these company events in the first place. I only knew that he had to be doing something really important.

When I first met George, I was on my way to work at my second job at the 45 local deli just down the street. He was on the way for a quick bite at the deli and we walked there together. When he found out that I was trying to supplement my income as a junior clerk at a law firm, he offered me a job. I was stunned when he told me that I would be paid three thousand dollars. That was way more than what I earned at the deli. I immediately agreed and even when he refused to reveal whom 50 he worked for and swore me to secrecy, I decided to take on the task. It sounded easy enough – spend time talking to the elderly man of a food and beverage company and keep him occupied throughout an entire dinner party. I was hooked and I took on one job after another since then.

However, this was the first time that George was late. Usually, he arrived soon 55 after me. I was wondering how to get the girl to leave when I noticed an elderly man at the other end of the room who seemed to be trying to catch the girl's attention. I pointed him out to her. She smiled brightly and walked over immediately. I caught George's eye and he strode over, his eyes darting at the girl who had just walked away. My heart sank. Was that the girl I was supposed to be chatting to? She didn't 60 look at all like she would be interested in talking about designer handbags. How would I even bring up the topic?

"That's Rachel. She's the daughter of the company director. Was she just talking to you? This is going to be tough. She can be quite flighty, moving from one guest to the next. Once she has spoken to you, she might ignore you for the rest of the night. Now, you've got to find a way to get her attention. I need that card." The last sentence he said with gritted teeth. I had never seen George so determined but my tasks had never been so challenging either. "I'll be at the corner where I can observe everything. Don't worry. I'll know when to approach. Just do what you have to do."

I racked my brains for a new disguise. I gazed at where she was, laughing and talking to a small group of guests. I contemplated milling around where she would probably be headed next, a small group of ladies who all looked like they were wearing different variations of the same outfit, but that would be drawing too much attention to myself. George said that I had to keep a low profile, be as discreet as I could and dress as nondescript as I could. "Do something," he hissed as he walked towards the bar, nodding and smiling at people as he walked like he knew them all when I doubted he did.

Just then, I noticed that Rachel's attention was focused on the bag that one of the ladies in the group was carrying. It was a pale orange fold over clutch with a round gold ring in the center. It was a limited edition Blighton, one that I had seen in a magazine recently. There were only a few of these in the world and the lady had one of them. Did Rachel want one as well or did she already have one? It was then that I noticed the Blighton clutch that Rachel was holding in midnight blue with a row of diamonds across the front and a ruby studded clasp over the triangular shaped cover. That was a limited edition one too. Years ago, I worked part time at a Blighton store when I was studying in the university. I knew all about their bags. Perhaps, I could engage in conversation with her after all. I was carrying one myself. It just wasn't a limited edition one but it was one of the more popular designs. All I needed was to get her attention and draw her away from the rest of the guests. It would be less tumultuous than before. As she walked towards the girl, George clenched his fists nervously. This was one of their most important missions.

Choose the correct answer and circle the correct letter.

 1 What does the author use in the first paragraph highlight an impending event?

    A   "tossed my hair back" (line 4)

    B   "Barely three minutes had passed" (line 7)

    C   "I never let my eyes rest on any one thing" (lines 4-5)

    D   "trying to look indifferent to my surroundings" (lines 2-3)

Sadlier School

2   What does the phrase "I must clarify" (line 10) have on the reader's impression of the author?

    A   The author was a timid person.

    B   The author was not a confident person.

    C   The author did not take her job seriously.

    D   The author wanted to complete her task quickly.

3   (a)   Which of the following is an example of the irony of the situation that the author was in at the start of the story?

    A   The author pretended not to know the girl who approached her.

    B   The author's fear helped her to be more observant of the people around her.

    C   The author's composure was a signal of her anxiety rather than her alertness.

    D   The author was supposed to be inconspicuous but the girl had walked up to her.

    (b)   Explain how the description of the surroundings is used to amplify the irony in Part A. Use details from the passage to support your answer.

_____

_____

_____

_____

_____

_____

_____

_____

_____

_____

_____

4   In paragraphs 3-5, why was information about the author's thoughts interspersed with events happening at the party?

    A   To add suspense to the story

    B   To complicate the plot of the story

    C   To tell the reader about the difficulties of being a spy

    D   To leave the reader with a better impression of the author

5 What was the main difference between the author's current mission and the mission at the last dinner party? Support your answer with one detail from the passage.

_____

_____

_____

_____

_____

_____

_____

_____

_____

_____

_____

_____

_____

6 The author said that "the spotlight shone right on George." (line 39) Why might this have been an inappropriate way for George to arrive?

A   The girl would be able to recognize him.

B   George would not be able to leave the party.

C   The author was supposed to have arrived with him.

D   He was supposed to be discreet to complete his mission.

7 Which of the following best supports the conclusion that the author wished she had not spoken to Rachel before George's arrival?

A   "I racked my brains for a new disguise." (line 69)

B   "Alarm bells rang in my head. I did not like the look on her face." (line 29)

C   "I shrugged, hoping that my feigned disinterest was working and she would leave me alone soon." (lines 16-17)

D   "However, when I was on a mission, I hated such rude interruptions to my train of thoughts or a lack of it." (lines 11-12)

8. Explain how the author made use of her alertness to carry out her mission. Use two details from the passage to support your answer.

_____

_____

_____

_____

_____

_____

_____

_____

_____

_____

9. Identify the differences between the author's and George's behaviors at the party. Explain how these might have affected the mission. Use details from the passage to support your answer. In your response, include
   • what the author did and explain how it benefited or affected the mission
   • what George did and how it benefited or affected the mission

_____

_____

_____

_____

_____

_____

_____

_____

_____

_____

(10) The author said that her mission would be "less tumultuous than before." (line 89) Did George and the author have similar thoughts? Use details from the passage to support your answer.

_____

_____

_____

_____

_____

_____

_____

_____

_____

_____

_____

Glossary

indifferent: not showing interest in someone or something
The basketball team had been losing every game but the coach was indifferent to the results.

feigned: to pretend to be doing something or to pretend to have a particular feeling
My sister feigned ignorance when I asked her if she was the one who had spoiled my game console.

espionage: refers to the use of spies to obtain secret information and giving the information to enemies
They were sentenced to lifetime imprisonment after admitting to committing espionage.

tete-a-tete: a private conversation
The president had a tete-a-tete with his private secretary before the dinner.

discreet: to be careful in what one says or does
I reminded her to be discreet when she was at the party and not draw attention to herself.

nondescript: ordinary and uninteresting
The billionaire was a humble man who lived in a nondescript house in the suburbs.

tumultuous: to have a lot of activity, confusion and disorder
She spent a few tumultuous years living in a homeless shelter until she was adopted by a caring family.

DATE: .... NAME: ....

CLASS: ....

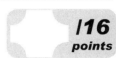

Read the passage carefully.

Life at Yessney

Sylvia Seltoun ate her breakfast in the morning-room at Yessney with a pleasant sense of ultimate victory. She was scarcely pugnacious by temperament. She belonged to that more successful class of fighters who were pugnacious by circumstance. Fate had willed that her life should be occupied with a series of small
5 struggles, usually with the odds slightly against her. Usually she had just managed to come through winning. Now she felt that she had succeeded with her hardest and certainly her most important struggle. To have married Mortimer Seltoun, in the teeth of the cold hostility of his family was indeed an achievement that had needed some determination and adroitness to carry through; yesterday she had brought
10 her victory to its concluding stage by wrenching her husband away from the town and "settling him down" in this remote manor farm which was his country house.

"You will never get Mortimer to go," his mother had said, "but if he goes, he'll stay; Yessney throws almost as much a spell over him as the town does. One can understand what holds him to the town, but Yessney…" and the dowager
15 had shrugged her shoulders and walked off as Sylvia had glared at her quiet but undisguised contempt.

There was a somber almost savage wildness about Yessney that was certainly not likely to appeal to town-bred tastes. Yet Sylvia looked on the country as something excellent and wholesome in its way. Outside the morning-room windows
20 was a triangular slope of turf, which the indulgent might call a lawn, and beyond its low hedge of neglected fuschia bushes a steeper slope of heather and bracken dropped down into combes overgrown with oak and yew. In its wild open savagery there seemed a stealthy linking of the joy of life with the terror of unseen things. Sylvia smiled complacently as she gazed with a School-of-Art appreciation at the
25 landscape, and then all of a sudden she almost shuddered.

"It is very wild," she said to Mortimer, who had joined her. "One could almost think that in such a place the worship of Pan had never quite died out." Sylvia was intrigued by Pan after reading about him, but she never quite believed the myths.

30 "The worship of Pan never has died out," said Mortimer. "He is the Nature-God to whom all must come back at last. He has been called the Father of all the Gods."

Sylvia was religious in an honest, vaguely devotional kind of way, and did not like to hear her beliefs spoken of as mere after growths, but it was at least something new and hopeful to hear Mortimer speak with such energy and conviction on any
35 subject.

"You don't really believe in Pan?" she asked incredulously.

"I've been a fool in most things," said Mortimer quietly, "but I'm not such a fool as not to believe in Pan when I'm down here. And if you're wise you won't disbelieve in him too boastfully while you're in his country."

40 It was not till a fortnight later, when Sylvia had exhausted the attractions of the woodland walks round Yessney, that she ventured on a tour of inspection of the farm buildings. It was a tour that she should have avoided given the circumstances. A farmyard suggested in her mind a scene of cheerful bustle with smiling dairymaids and teams of horses drinking knee-deep in duck-crowded ponds. As she wandered
45 among the gaunt gray buildings of Yessney manor farm, her first impression was one of crushing stillness and desolation. It was as though she had happened on some lone deserted homestead long given over to owls and cobwebs; then came a sense of furtive watchful hostility, the same shadow of unseen things that seemed to lurk in the wooded combes and coppices. The nefarious mood was gradually emerging
50 from behind the shadows. At last, turning a corner quickly, she came upon a living thing. Lying stretched out in a pool of mud was an enormous sow. Sylvia did her best to make an unobtrusive retreat. As she threaded her way past rickyards and cowsheds and long blank walls, she started suddenly at a strange sound - the echo of a boy's laughter, golden and equivocal. Jan, the only boy employed on the farm, a
55 wizen-faced child, was visibly at work on a potato clearing half-way up the nearest hill-side. Mortimer, when questioned, knew of no probable reason for the hidden mockery that had ambushed Sylvia's retreat.

Of Mortimer she saw very little; farm and woods and trout- streams seemed to swallow him up from dawn till dusk. Even when she asked for him to be around
60 that day when she was feeling under the weather, he had placed the medicine on the night table before hurriedly leaving the house. He came back at lunch but only to repeat his actions. Then, he was gone again.

* * **101** * * *
Exercise 15

Sadlier School

Once, taking the direction she had seen him take after following him more than once in the morning, she came to an open space in the center of which stood a stone pedestal surmounted by a small bronze figure of a youthful Pan. It was a beautiful piece of workmanship, but her attention was chiefly held by the fact that a newly cut bunch of grapes had been placed as an offering at its feet. Grapes were none too plentiful at the manor house, and Sylvia snatched the bunch angrily from the pedestal. Annoyance dominated her thoughts as she strolled slowly homeward, but this then gave way to a sharp feeling of something that was very near fright; across a thick tangle of undergrowth a boy's face was scowling at her. Sylvia sped forward without waiting to give a closer scrutiny to this sudden apparition. It was not till she had reached the house that she discovered that she had dropped the bunch of grapes in her flight.

"I saw a youth in the woods today," she told Mortimer that evening after they had finished dinner, "brown-faced and rather handsome, but a scoundrel to look at. A gypsy lad, I suppose."

"A reasonable theory," said Mortimer, "only there aren't any gypsies in these parts at present."

"Then who was he?" asked Sylvia, and as Mortimer appeared to have no theory of his own she passed on to recount her finding of the offering.

"I suppose it was your doing," she observed; "it's a harmless piece of lunacy, but people would think you dreadfully silly if they knew of it."

"Did you meddle with it in any way?" asked Mortimer.

"I…I threw the grapes away. It seemed so silly," said Sylvia, watching Mortimer's impassive face for a sign of annoyance.

"I don't think you were wise to do that," he said reflectively. "I've heard it said that Pan can be rather horrible to those who disrespect him."

"I don't believe in that," retorted Sylvia.

"All the same," said Mortimer in his even tone, "I should give a wide berth to the woods and orchards if I were you.

Sylvia noted with dissatisfaction and some self-contempt that the course of her next afternoon's ramble took her instinctively clear of the network of woods.

(Adapted from The Music on the Hill by Saki)

Sadlier School

Choose the correct answer and circle the correct letter.

1. What effect does the author create by starting the story with reference to Sylvia's "ultimate victory" (line 2)?

   A   Clear understanding of events prior to the story

   B   Gain in-depth understanding of Sylvia's personality

   C   Anticipation of what the story will be as a result of the victory

   D   Expectation of great rivalry between the characters in the story

2. Which of the following supports the conclusion that Sylvia was not an apathetic person?

   A   "She was scarcely pugnacious by temperament." (line 2)

   B   "She belonged to that more successful class of fighters who were pugnacious by circumstance." (lines 3-4)

   C   "Now she felt that she had succeeded with her hardest and certainly her most important struggle." (lines 6-7)

   D   "Fate had willed that her life should be occupied with a series of small struggles, usually with the odds slightly against her." (lines 4-5)

3. (a) What does "cold hostility" (line 8) tell you about Sylvia's relationship with Mortimer's family?

   A   She did not know them well.

   B   She did not get along with them.

   C   She had known them for a long time.

   D   She was not willing to speak to them.

   (b) What could have resulted in the "cold hostility" between Sylvia and Mortimer's family? Support your answer with a detail from the passage.

   _____

   _____

   _____

   _____

   _____

   _____

   _____

   _____

   _____

   _____

4 What does the phrase "wrenching her husband away from the town" (line 10) reveal about Sylvia's personality?

  A She was a stern and argumentative person.

  B She did not think before she made decisions

  C She had little regard for other people's feelings.

  D She would try her utmost to achieve what she wanted.

5 Explain how the author shows the contradictions in Yessney in paragraph 3. Support your answer with details from the paragraph.

_____

_____

_____

_____

_____

_____

_____

_____

_____

_____

_____

_____

_____

_____

_____

_____

_____

_____

_____

_____

_____

6 Sylvia revealed different opinions of Pan when she first arrived in the country with Mortimer. How did these opinions differ from those held by Mortimer? Support your answer with details from the passage. In your response
- Identify Sylvia's and Mortimer's opinions of Pan
- How the opinions differed

_____

_____

_____

_____

_____

_____

_____

_____

_____

_____

_____

_____

_____

_____

_____

_____

7 (a) Which of the following is the best summary of paragraph 8?

    A   "The nefarious mood was gradually emerging from behind the shadows." (lines 49-50)

    B   "It was a tour that she should have avoided given the circumstances." (line 42)

    C   "Mortimer, when questioned, knew of no probable reason for the hidden mockery that had ambushed Sylvia's retreat." (lines 56-57)

    D   "As she wandered among the gaunt grey buildings of Yessney manor farm, her first impression was one of crushing stillness and desolation." (lines 44-46) (b)　Support your answer in Part A using details from the paragraph.

_____

_____

_____

_____

_____

_____

_____

_____

_____

_____

8 (a)　What effect does the author create with the phrase "swallow him up" (line 59) on the reader's understanding of Mortimer's activities?

A　They completely absorbed him.

B　They were difficult to understand.

C　They were dull everyday activities.

D　They were mysterious and interesting.

(b)　What evidence does the author provide to support the answer in Part A?

_____

_____

_____

_____

_____

_____

_____

_____

_____

9 The author states that Sylvia felt something that was "very near fright" (line 71) when she saw the boy's face in the undergrowth. Explain why the subsequent events both supported and contradicted this description. Support your answer with details from the passage.

_____

_____

_____

_____

_____

_____

_____

_____

_____

_____

10 The story reveals a relationship between the god, Pan, and the effect he has on the people living in the wilderness. Explain how the author shows the dominating effects of Pan. Support your answer with details from the passage.

_____

_____

_____

_____

_____

_____

_____

_____

_____

_____

_____

pugnacious: referring to a person who is eager to argue with others
His pugnacious manner made it difficult to hold a conversation with him for long.

hostile: to behave in an unfriendly manner towards others
The basketball player was given a hostile reception after the match as he had played badly during the game.

adroit: referring to someone who is skillful in the way he uses words in an argument
Only those who are adroit negotiators will be called to the scene of the crime to try to dissuade the perpetrator from hurting his victims.

somber: serious and sad mood
There was a somber mood in the country after the death of their beloved king was announced.

vague: unclear
If you are vague about your role in the project, you should clarify it with the manager before the project commences.

nefarious: referring to something that is evil or criminal
His nefarious activities will soon catch up with him and he will be put behind bars.

equivocal: uncertain and unclear
The government's response to the new policy was equivocal. It was unclear what their stand was.

wizen: to be lean and wrinkled
He was a wizen man who had undergone years of hardship traveling from country to country.

even: calm
The health officer replied all the questions in an even tone despite the increasing agitation from the audience.

ramble: a hike
She went for a ramble on her own whenever she could as she enjoyed spending time among nature.